GROWING TOMATOES

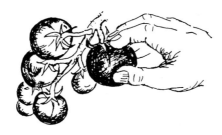

IAN G. WALLS

DAVID & CHARLES
Newton Abbot · London

British Library Cataloguing in Publication Data

Walls, Ian G. (Ian Gascoigne), *1922–*
  Growing tomatoes.
  1. Tomatoes. Cultivation
  I. Title
  635'.642

ISBN 0-7153-9128-3

Typeset by Typesetters (Birmingham) Ltd
Smethwick Warley West Midlands
and printed in Great Britain by
Redwood Burn Limited, Trowbridge, Wilts
for David & Charles Publishers plc
Brunel House Newton Abbot Devon

Colour origination by Columbia Offset (UK) Ltd

Contents

Author's Note 4

Introduction 5

1 The Basic Requirements for Tomato Culture 6

2 Greenhouse Equipment 25

3 The Physiology of the Tomato Plant 41

4 Soil, Nutrients and Growing Media 58

5 Propagation 74

6 An Examination of Cultural Methods 91

7 Pre-planting Procedures 107

8 Planting 123

9 Establishment and Training 130

10 General Growing Procedures 141

11 Diseases, Pests and Physiological 153
    or Nutritional Disorders

12 Sterilisation of Soil, and Other Growing Media 174

13 Tomato Varieties 179

14 Outdoor Tomatoes 182

Appendices

1 The Economics of Tomato Production 186

2 Tomato Grading 190

3 Nutrient Film Technique (NFT), Mineral 190
    Rockwool Culture and Perlite Culture

4 Useful Addresses 194

5 Getting Advice 197

Index 198

Author's Note

When I wrote *Tomato Growing Today*, published in 1972, there had not been appreciable change in tomato-growing methods for a great many years. Systems of culture based on peat, including growbags, were relatively new on the scene and there had been no real takeup of other present-day systems such as rockwool, perlite or nutrient film technique (NFT). Commercial growers and really keen gardeners were still sterilising their soils with steam or chemicals, little realising perhaps that profound changes were imminent. Yields, too, especially in commercial circles were but a fraction of what they are today and yields of 46lb per sq yd (260 tonnes/ha) were talked about in bated breath as the sheer pinnacle of success.

Now, in the late 1980s, things have changed dramatically, both in commercial and in amateur growing circles. Few commercial growers now steam-sterilise their soils or, for that matter, use the borders at all, having been gradually weaned on to various systems independent of border soils and the residual problems they may contain. The same can be said for amateur gardeners, as there has been a massive takeup of growbags and other systems not dependent on the soil in greenhouse borders. Exceptions are, perhaps, the organic growers who will still faithfully use the greenhouse border copiously dressed with compost but on a planned rotation. Otherwise there is today a considerable marriage between commercial systems and amateur systems of growing in many spheres and this certainly includes tomatoes.

However, commercialism being what it is today, growers and gardeners alike can all too easily fall into the trap of thinking that something which is well advertised must be good. Perhaps it is for this reason that one hears so little about tomato grafting on to resistant rootstocks, or straw-bale systems of tomato culture, being less publicised because there is so little material to sell involved. I always hesitate about including economic information in any book, as it is something which dates so quickly because of inflation, nor indeed is the amateur gardener too much concerned about the cost of growing. Yet it seems in this materialistic world in which we live that something should be said about economics and this has been done.

Finally, any author writing about tomato growing these days must obviously draw on the experience of others because there are so many variances in cultural techniques, and this I have done. Let me therefore thank those individuals and firms who have enabled me to produce this book on tomato growing as, without their collective help, the task would have been impossible.

IAN G. WALLS
Milngavie

Introduction

Tomatoes are without doubt one of the most important and popular salad crops in many countries around the world. Indeed, it is true to say that it would be a poor salad bowl without a tomato. While the culture of tomatoes can be relatively simple, there are many details surrounding their culture which, if understood, help to produce bigger and better crops of fruit. *Growing Tomatoes* looks systematically and realistically at the culture of tomatoes, and in considerable detail, and relates this to the systems of culture which are popular today, not only in domestic greenhouses but in commercial concerns.

The earlier chapters deal in general terms with the requirements for growing tomatoes, especially in cooler climates where it is generally necessary to provide a warmer and more congenial atmosphere in order to produce bigger crops of quality fruits. The precise physical and nutritional needs of tomatoes are then discussed in some detail, followed by methods of plant raising and the composts and containers best used for this. Various cultural methods are then compared and evaluated, before moving on to the actual culture of the crop – planting, watering, feeding and plant training – and the other essential elements which will contribute to success. Modern varieties of tomato are also looked at, and there is a detailed section on some of the troubles which may beset the crop and how best to rectify these. For the more serious grower there is a section dealing with the economics of the crop in modern terms.

To summarise, therefore, this book is as complete an epistle on the culture of tomatoes as anyone with aspirations to grow the crop well is likely to need.

1
The Basic Requirements
for Tomato Culture

The precise genealogy of the tomato, if one may use that word in the botanical field, is something which fascinates many gardeners. Most gardeners do, I feel I appreciate that the tomato is a warm-bodied plant, native to tropical America. It was originally eaten by the people of Mexico and called '*tomati*'. It was known in Europe in the sixteenth century, mainly as an ornamental plant, and this persisted until the latter part of the eighteenth century when it became recognised as an edible vegetable, but it does not appear to have become popular for culinary purposes in Europe until the middle of the nineteenth century.

Tomatoes belong to the natural order Solanaceae and belong to the genus *Lycopersicon*. According to Bailey (1924), there are several varieties of *Lycopersicon esculentum*: *commune*, common tomato; *grandiflorum*, large-leaved tomato; *validium*, upright tomato; *cerasiforme*, cherry tomato; and *pyriforme*, pear tomato. Since tomatoes were first categorised botanically, there has been a considerable amount of breeding work, sparked off perhaps by astute growers such as Alan Balch in Ayrshire at the turn of this century when he produced the famous 'Ailsa Craig' variety of tomatoes. In recent years plant breeders have concentrated on the breeding of high-yielding varieties with specific shapes or sizes of fruit, with specific habits of growth, and with introduced resistances to various pests and diseases. The situation is a constantly changing one, with newer varieties being produced all the time, although there has been a gradual slowing-up of breeding work so far as the United Kingdom is concerned in the last year or two, as the quantities of seed required by industry are not as large as they were.

While many of the newer commercial varieties are now available to amateurs, many gardeners prefer to stick to older, well-tried varieties. Most of the newer varieties available in the UK are hybrids but there is still a great love for what is called 'straight' varieties of which 'Ailsa Craig' is typical.

Commercial production of tomatoes in the EEC countries and further afield shows some degree of parity between the top producers, Holland and Italy, bearing in mind that much of the Italian production is out of doors. These countries are followed by Spain, Greece and Portugal in that order. Britain is well down the scale for tomato production but the tomato is, nevertheless, a very important glasshouse crop in Britain, taking up somewhat over 1,500 acres (600ha) of which approximately one-third is for the lucrative early crop.

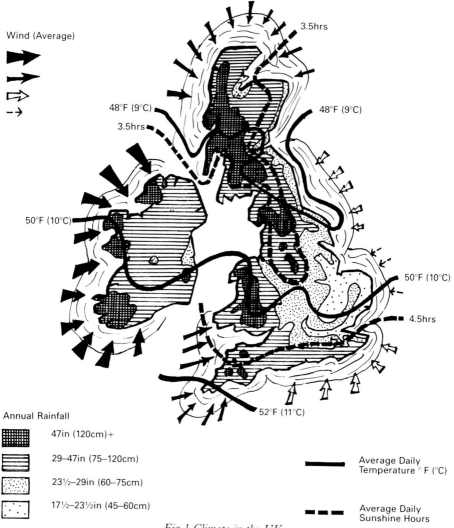

Wind (Average)

3.5hrs

48°F (9°C)

3.5hrs

48°F (9°C)

50°F (10°C)

50°F (10°C)

4.5hrs

52°F (11°C)

Annual Rainfall

47in (120cm)+

29–47in (75–120cm)

23½–29in (60–75cm)

17½–23½in (45–60cm)

Average Daily
Temperature ° F (°C)

Average Daily
Sunshine Hours

Fig 1 Climate in the UK

Official statistics always tend to be somewhat out of date, however, and it must be appreciated that the situation regarding areas under cultivation is a changing one.

It is interesting to speculate how many tomatoes are grown in amateur greenhouses in Britain and, for that matter, other countries. The figure must be a staggering one. In commercial terms, yields have, as stated earlier, risen dramatically and, although many amateur gardeners do tend to treat tomatoes as a short-term crop, grown cold and very subject to variation in weather patterns, it seems likely that yields in amateur greenhouses are also increasing with improved growing methods.

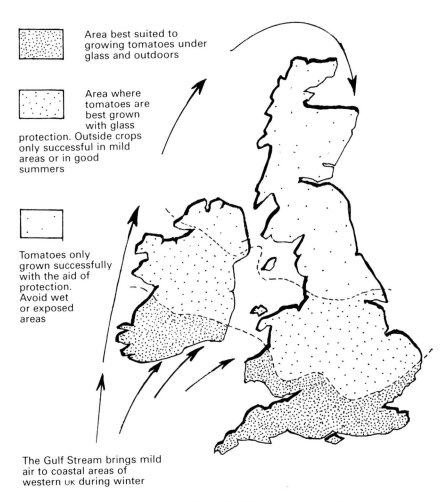

Area best suited to growing tomatoes under glass and outdoors

Area where tomatoes are best grown with glass protection. Outside crops only successful in mild areas or in good summers

Tomatoes only grown successfully with the aid of protection. Avoid wet or exposed areas

The Gulf Stream brings mild air to coastal areas of western UK during winter

Fig 2 Tomato growing in the UK as it relates to climate

WHERE TO GROW TOMATOES

It is remarkable what a variation in climate there can be from district to district in the UK, and it is only when one begins to look at weather studies in detail that this becomes apparent, and one sees the considerable variation in light intensities, average temperatures and exposure to winds that there is. Any commercial grower proposing to set up in business and grow tomatoes for profit would obviously have to take weather factors very much into account, but it is doubtful if the average gardener is so concerned. Nevertheless, for the seriously minded person, anxious to produce maximum crops of tomatoes, either for home use or for sale, some study of climatic factors would be well worth while. The rainfall incidence obviously has an effect not only on light intensity but in humidity of the atmosphere, and gardeners in high rainfall areas, with their attendant high humidities, must be well aware of the problems brought about by excess humidity in the shape of botrytis and physiological disorders generally (*see* Chapter 11). An interesting issue related to location is the choice of growing method. Certain systems of culture such as the straw-bale or straw-wad method quite obviously create higher humidity than do growbags, and it is worth bearing this in mind when it comes to choosing the most effective cultural method.

Climate apart, and bearing in mind that the west of the UK is generally warmer and more humid than the east, artificial heat is certainly necessary for the propagation stage of tomatoes, no matter how they are later cultivated, the exception being a really late crop which can be propagated without any artificial heat, provided the weather is co-operative. Really late crops are likely to be light ones unless artificial heat is available for the plants so that they carry on cropping well into the autumn months. How much heat one is prepared to use depends on what production programme is selected and how this fits into the district in question. There can be no doubt that, in Britain as a whole, if yields are to be both reasonable and dependable, the use of artificial heat is more or less essential as we will see later.

LIGHT

Temperature patterns are fairly closely related to light intensity, not only to the total 'bright sunshine' registered by meteorological stations, but to total radiation, which is bright sunshine plus diffused light. In other words, an area with higher bright-sunshine figures usually enjoys higher total radiation in consequence. In winter, in northern climes, the available natural light falls well below the requirements for vegetative development and the production of fertile pollen followed by successful fertilisation of the tomato plant. The winter sunshine figures between 1921 and 1950 as recorded by meteorological stations can be seen in the table below.

Winter Sunshine Hours 1921–50							
	Oct	*Nov*	*Dec*	*Jan*	*Feb*	*Mar*	*Total*
Regent's Park	83	41	27	29	47	92	319
Enfield	97	50	35	40	61	114	397
Kew	95	51	39	42	60	112	399
Wye	113	64	51	53	75	134	490
Bognor Regis	122	75	63	67	83	142	552
Plymouth (Mt Batten)	114	70	55	57	76	136	508
Blackpool	96	54	37	44	66	117	414
Hull	95	48	31	33	57	97	369
Renfrew	74	43	28	31	53	93	322
NB Light levels in urban areas much improved since 'Clean Air Act'.							

Poor winter sunshine is of course one reason why artificial lighting has been so universally adopted by specialised tomato growers (*see* Chapter 2).

It is interesting to note that where there is a large bulk of water, either coastal or inland, total radiation figures are higher, as reflected light is added to the direct light. An area free of smoke pollution and not subject to fog will also enjoy higher total radiation figures, not only because of the unrestricted passage of light through the atmosphere, but because there is less staining of glass or polythene. Hills, buildings or trees must also be taken into account in any area, as these can shut off the sun (*see also below*).

NUTRITION

There must, on a growing tomato plant, be roots capable of sustaining foliage, flower and fruit development, and these roots must be sufficiently healthy and unaffected by pest or disease, otherwise the whole growing process is either arrested or slowed down, a situation by no means uncommon (*see* Chapter 11). Adequate nutrition is also essential, especially for the plant bearing a heavy crop of swelling fruit, this sometimes without the assistance of a normal complement of foliage, much of which is frequently removed under modern training methods. Nutrition is considered in detail in Chapter 3.

GREENHOUSES

There must be compromise in most things, and this certainly applies to the choice and siting of a greenhouse for the growing of tomatoes. The selection of a good, light area, a flat site, good drainage, adequate water and power supplies; the choice of a design allowing for maximum light transmission; and the installation of automatic heating, heat conservation, watering, ventilating and feeding systems are all-important issues for the serious grower.

Yet to most gardeners a garden, yard or greenhouse is an adjunct to the dwelling house, which is selected on many considerations, often mainly congenial living conditions and reasonable proximity to place of business. Enthusiastic gardeners however may be strongly influenced in their choice of house or site by the horticultural potentialities of the garden, especially if they have commercial aspirations.

Selecting a Greenhouse

The perplexities of selecting a greenhouse with tomato culture largely in mind are many. Light and heat from the sun are highly important, and it is advisable to think in terms of an all-glass type of structure where the supports are minimal, though consistent with adequate strength. This usually means having little or no base wall, whether of brick, wood or asbestos. The tomato, though undoubtedly a tall crop, demands light for its full life and especially when newly planted out, and base walls tend to reduce light transmission to the young plants, particularly if the greenhouse is narrow.

Frequently the tomato crop is Cinderella to the overwintering of potplants and dormant tubers, followed by some varied early-season propagation. Such

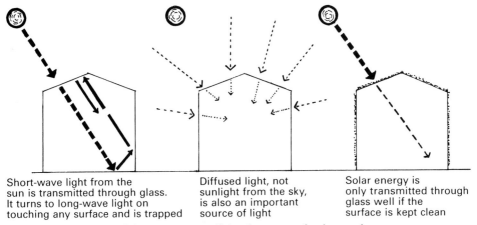

Short-wave light from the sun is transmitted through glass. It turns to long-wave light on touching any surface and is trapped

Diffused light, not sunlight from the sky, is also an important source of light

Solar energy is only transmitted through glass well if the surface is kept clean

Fig 3 Solar energy – an efficient heat source for the greenhouse

activities demand constant heat and certainly 100 per cent frost protection during the winter months. All forms of artificial heat cost money and, as the chief value of glass is its ability to transmit solar light and heat, it follows that glass is a poor insulator and does not readily conserve heat when solar radiation ceases.

In effect, therefore, the more glass in any structure, the higher the heating costs, and while the all-glass structure can provide optimal conditions for tomato growing in so far as light transmission is concerned, one has to be prepared to pay for the artificial heat necessary. This heating may be necessary throughout the winter for the other purposes referred to, and it may be preferable therefore to select a base-wall type of greenhouse which will obviously be less costly to heat especially throughout the winter months. Where cold growing is intended and the cost of artificial heat of no consequence, then an all-glass greenhouse should be chosen.

Orientation of the greenhouse

The following remarks apply to the northern hemisphere.

Simply because a greenhouse has a high proportion of glass to opaque material, this does not ensure the best possible light transmission. Glass has reflective qualities and transmits maximum solar light and heat only when the angle of incidence is normal (90°) or nearly so. The angle of the sun in the sky does, as we all know, vary considerably, not only between morning and evening but also according to season. In the winter the sun is in the sky for very brief periods and the low angle of incidence of its rays on the earth's surface is such that heat and light rays are deflected from all but the nearly vertical sides or ends of a greenhouse. Much of the solar radiation is certainly deflected from the normally angled roof of a conventionally shaped greenhouse. It may be difficult to appreciate this phenomenon simply by using the eye as a measuring device, yet light-sensitive plants will certainly register their protest by showing drawn or etiolated growth, a frequent state of affairs with light-loving houseplants in the home. The light-transmission

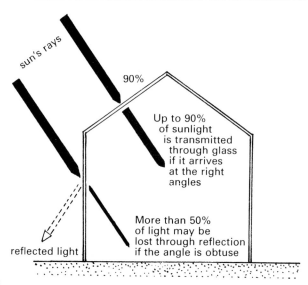

Fig 4 The reflection of the sun's rays on a glasshouse

qualities of a greenhouse can, of course, be measured by instruments such as light meters or even modern cameras. Tomatoes are particularly sensitive to light intensity, especially during the early part of the year.

It follows, therefore, that when winter light is particularly desirable, as it is for young tomatoes (or for most other propagation activities), it is important to site a greenhouse with its long axis running east–west so that the maximum area of glass is presented favourably to the low-angled winter sun. As the sun rises on the horizon the south-facing roof slope gradually absorbs most of the solar light and heat, but any obstruction to the sun on the south side of the greenhouse, such as densely planted tomatoes when they get larger or other tall crops, will shade plants at the rear of the greenhouse. With the average-sized amateur greenhouse, however, this is not usually a major consideration. Nor is it a problem with the timetable which many amateur gardeners follow. If a greenhouse is sited with the ridge running north–south, only the south-facing gabled end is suitably angled to absorb winter light. When however the sun is higher on the horizon, from spring to autumn, there is more equal light distribution from the east in the morning and from the west in the afternoon and evening, and this has its advantages. On balance, however, there is much to be said for an east–west siting for the single greenhouse.

Greenhouse Shape

A considerable amount of research has taken place over many years on the best configuration of a greenhouse for maximum light transmission, winter and summer. In commercial circles, unevenly angled houses with steeper south-sloping roofs have been experimented with, as also have mansard-shaped greenhouses. In amateur circles, circular-type or geodesic houses have now

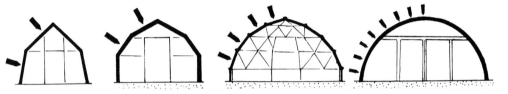

Fig 5 Glasshouses or plastic structures with many angled surfaces offer greater opportunities for maximum light admission

been on the market for some years, but I cannot feel that they have a great part to play in tomato culture, other than for the propagation period when they would certainly be extremely valuable. Mansard-type greenhouses are also readily available in amateur sizes. The increasing use of lean-to or conservatory types of greenhouses raises siting problems as they tend to overheat during the summer months if facing south. Of interest here is the 'Northern Light' Serac structure.

There is, in any case, usually more than adequate light for tomatoes during the summer months, in any structure, the really vital periods being during winter, spring and autumn; more will be said about this later (*see* Chapter 2). Sun shut-off occasioned by hills, buildings or trees should be looked out for. I have frequently come across excellent greenhouses or conservatories situated in a particular location in the garden where a tree shades off the sun for several hours each day – although this is not necessarily a great disadvantage in high summer.

Provision of Shelter

Exposure to wind is a matter of considerable importance, as (as well as causing structural damage) it can reduce the average temperature in the greenhouse by accentuating heat loss; it also raises the fuel bill. Periods of low temperature resulting from the failure to take exposure into account impose an inevitable growth check which can be very damaging to the tomato crop (*see* Chapter 3). Outdoor culture would, of course, be similarly affected by exposure.

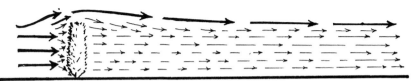

A permeable hedge reduces wind speed over a distance of up to ten times its height behind the hedge

A solid barrier like a wall can cause wind turbulence which may damage glasshouses or structures

Fig 6 The importance of permeable windbreaks, like hedges, in reducing wind speed

Artificial Shelter Media	
Type	Comments
Plastic trellis	clean, long lasting
Wood trellis	shorter term, cheaper
Hollow blocks	great possibilities
Netlon	portable, very effective
Horizontal canes	quite effective
Vertical canes	quite effective
Offset slats (wood)	offer privacy also
Wire netting and straw	effective but treat with black paint
Vertical lath (wood)	must be treated
Horizontal lath (wood)	must be treated
Single-layer slats (wood)	very impressive looking
Interwoven fencing (wood)	needs heavy support if exposed
Polypropylene	rot resistant
Rokoline	effective and attractive
Paraweb (ici). Nicofence (Clovis Lande/ Garden Rewards*)	very effective if well erected

Natural Shelter Media	
Type	Comments
Hedges	
Myrobalan (*Prunus cerasifera*)	
Prunus pissardii nigra	
Holly (common form)	
Yew	make thick imprenetrable hedges up to
Privet	2–2¼m (6–8ft) and require regular cutting
Beech	
Hornbeam	
Quickthorn	
Willow (kept as hedge)	
All take time to develop	
Trees	
Silver birch	
Larch	
Picea excelsa and *sitchensis*	
Poplars, Italian	
Limes	Make effective shelter belts if sufficient
Mountain Ash	room for development but rather long term
Pinus sylvestris	
Conifer hedges	
Chamaecyparis lawsoniana	
Cupressocyparis leylandii	Make tall hedges up to 6m (20ft) or more
Thuja lobbii and *excelsa*	but also longer term

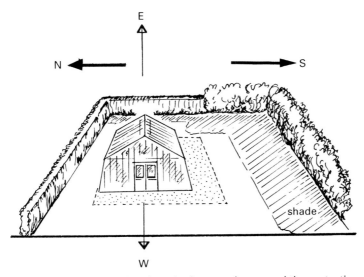

The distance between the plants in the greenhouse and the protecting treeline (on the south side) should be at least twice the height of the treeline to avoid shadow being cast over the glass. The correct site is shown by the dotted area – close to the north hedge, but protected from wind by the southern treeline

Fig 7 The orientation and positioning of greenhouses

Provision of shelter is often therefore a necessity, either by the use of artificial screening material or by the planting of hedges or tree belts – provided these are at a sufficient distance to avoid sun shut-off or root problems. It is now accepted that a 50 per cent permeable shelter-material is more efficient than a solid one, as it does not create turbulence. A screen or hedge should provide effective shelter over a distance of approximately ten to fifteen times its height.

Further Aspects of Greenhouse Selection and Siting

Other issues of some importance regarding greenhouse selection are: width of doors to allow ready access; sufficient headroom; constructional materials; and glazing systems of such a type to avoid constant maintenance – this I feel being of paramount importance. There must also be adequate provision for heat-saving methods. Ventilation must be adequate to avoid overheating and excess humidity. Vents should preferably be on both sides of the ridge, with side vents in addition.

The danger of warping or distortion is also an important point to bear in mind; it is for this reason that aluminium-alloy greenhouses are enjoying such popularity, although I see nothing wrong with a well-constructed wooden house, provided it incorporates a grooved glazing system and that superior or properly pressure-treated wood is used. Indeed they can be ideal for tomato growing providing, as they do, an excellent environment and tending to be slightly warmer than aluminium houses. Other metal-type houses also have distinct virtues, provided the metal is well treated to avoid corrosion. Listed below are the various structural materials and their virtues or otherwise.

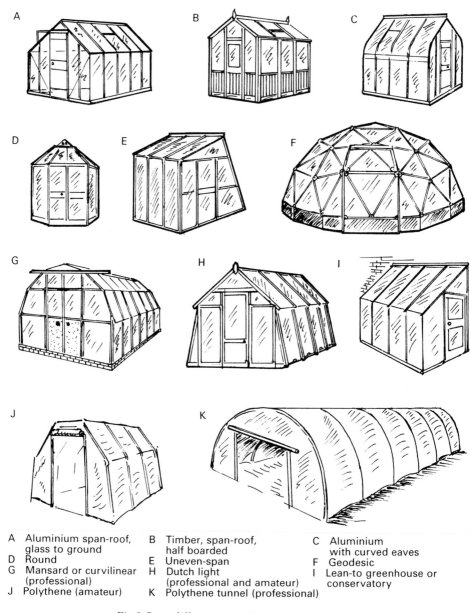

A   Aluminium span-roof,   B   Timber, span-roof,   C   Aluminium
    glass to ground   half boarded   with curved eaves
D   Round   E   Uneven-span   F   Geodesic
G   Mansard or curvilinear   H   Dutch light   I   Lean-to greenhouse or
    (professional)   (professional and amateur)   conservatory
J   Polythene (amateur)   K   Polythene tunnel (professional)

Fig 8 Some different types of greenhouse available

Structural Materials
Pine: difficult to treat with preservative
Redwood: good if painted or treated
Red cedar: good but not strong
Hardwoods: good but expensive
Burma teak: very good, also expensive
Pressure-treated softwoods: cheap and fairly good if well treated with preservatives
Steel: must be galvanised or otherwise treated
Cast iron: less liable to rust than steel but seldom used these days
Aluminium alloy: good in every respect

Always follow erection plans carefully. If levelling a site by one or other of the methods available (cut-and-fill, or levelling to highest or lowest point) always allow a period for subsidence. Ensure that there is adequate drainage, especially on a sloping site where water from higher land could be a severe problem for border tomato growing. It is also highly important that the subsoil should not be unduly consolidated during the levelling procedure, otherwise drainage could be further affected.

Control of bad weeds in the erection area must be carefully carried out, remembering that any chemical used for control purposes will not readily wash out of the greenhouse border once the area is covered by the greenhouse. It is therefore advisable to treat the bed some time prior to erection. The same is true of plastic structures (*see below*).

Adequate supplies of water and electricity are essential. There should also be collection of, or drainage for, water shed from roofs where this is likely to be a problem.

Mobile Greenhouses

Any account of tomato culture would be incomplete without a reference to greenhouse structures that can easily be moved to allow a crop rotation system and thereby avoid the problems of monoculture – for soil sickness invariably results from cropping continuously with tomatoes on the same site. With the renewed emphasis on organic growing methods, mobile greenhouses will, I feel sure, come back into prominence as they do allow for crop rotation.

Simple Dutch light greenhouses on temporary base-block 'walls', or complete, light, sectional greenhouses of any type, can of course be readily moved around the garden. This is perhaps even more true of plastic structures, particularly as the plastic requires fairly regular renewal in any case.

For a period after the last war there was a great vogue in commercial-size greenhouses capable of movement on rails or wheels inset on 'dollies', and mobile houses of some types are still available if specially requested. It is interesting to note that mobile greenhouses were first used in Britain during the early part of the century, not only for tomatoes but for tobacco. The only

1 Plastic structures have an increasing role for smaller-scale tomato culture. The Sungrow from 'Garden Rewards' is shaped to catch maximum sunlight and allow snow to slip off without causing damage

2 The Solardome structure ('Clovis Lande' and 'Garden Rewards') gives a lot of room for tomatoes or other crops, and is ideal for areas where there is little risk of heavy snowfall

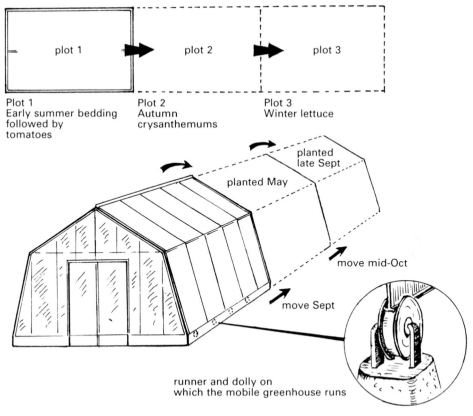

Plot 1
Early summer bedding
followed by
tomatoes

Plot 2
Autumn
crysanthemums

Plot 3
Winter lettuce

planted
late Sept

planted May

move mid-Oct

move Sept

runner and dolly on
which the mobile greenhouse runs

Fig 9 Mobile greenhouses allow for maximum use of glass, to protect several crops at critical growth stages.

type likely to interest the amateur, however, is a Dutch light structure with pulley wheels, runners and dollys, or running on rails set in the base blocks.

Any type of mobile structure does, of course, allow crop rotation by permitting the house to be moved *en bloc* over a predetermined number of plots, with obvious advantages where border culture is concerned. But higher initial cost of structure, plus the problem of a practicable form of heating and provision of other services, are disadvantages which must be carefully considered.

The efficiency of modern soil sterilants, coupled with the increasing number of possible cultural methods, plus the development of plastic structures, have tended to make mobile houses much less attractive.

Plastic Structures

There is a great deal of misleading or confusing information disseminated about plastic greenhouses and the following is an up-to-date account of their design and use for tomato culture. I was closely involved in the early designs of plastic greenhouses a considerable number of years ago when what could be called the 'plastic cult' developed in Britain. Gardeners have long utilised light-transmitting plastic materials to protect plants, but a basic fault with most of the earlier types of plastics was their limited life due to the destructive action of ultra-violet light. The net effect was that the early plastics tended to go cloudy and brittle. The main type of plastics in thin-film form used for horticultural production for many years has been polyvinyl chloride (PVC) and polythene (poly-ethylene). Other types are now available.

Various specifications of these materials started to be used in horticulture in the 1950s and I can recall growers and gardeners knocking together plastic structures constructed with wooden frameworks over which was tacked PVC or polythene. At that time Mr W.D. Way of Fordingbridge was one of the pioneers in using plastic greenhouses in large scale at his nursery in Barnham in Sussex, and I took parties of Scottish growers down to see his basic designs. Since those early days a lot has happened. Chemical firms such as ICI spent a great deal of time and money on research into plastics and, as far as the horticultural industry is concerned, they have tended to concentrate on polythene and the introduction of ultra-violet inhibitors (UVI) to this. They were by no means the only chemical company undertaking research, and other forms of thin-film plastics were being developed and tested. Obviously the economics of using thin-film plastics had to be investigated along with all the various technical issues involved.

Many gardeners assume that thin-film plastics respond in a similar way to glass in the transmission of solar radiation but this is not strictly so. Short-wave radiation from the sun passes through glass to be reflected back by the floor, ground, benches, and plants themselves as long-wave radiation which is effectively trapped by glass. Heat can therefore build up in a glasshouse and be retained for some time. In the case of the normal type of PVC and polythene, reflected long-wave radiation passes out much more readily, more so with polythene than with PVC. Manufacturers are looking very closely at materials for coating the thin-film plastic to reduce this loss of radiation heat and some types are now on the market, although their longevity in terms of ultra-violet breakdown would still seem to be in doubt. Research however is still going on and no doubt changes will be brought about if needed.

The net effect is that thin-film plastic structures provide a cooler growing regime than a glasshouse. A lot more condensation can also form on the inside surface of thin-film plastics, resulting in a rise in humidity, which can be ideal for many aspects of propagation and for some crops, but can cause problems for crops such as tomatoes which are very subject to high humidity-related diseases such as botrytis (*see* Chapter 11).

Light transmission through various plastic materials tends to be lower than through glass and it must also be borne in mind that, by the time the light filters through the plastic, it is diffused rather than direct. The effect of this slightly lower transmission may be noticeable earlier in the year but less so as the season progresses. However, the shape and orientation of plastic greenhouses is not so critical as it is with a glasshouse because most plastics tend to have less reflective qualities than glass.

There are of course rigid forms of plastics now on the market and these include PVC and polycarbonates, the latter being available in double- or treble-wall forms. When one moves from thin-film plastics to rigid plastics the cost of erection can rise, but there are obviously considerable advantages in using some of the rigid forms of plastic, especially bi-walled polycarbonate, as they reduce heat loss very considerably compared to either glass or single-film plastics. Light transmission is marginally reduced.

To return to the basic design of thin-film plastic structures, the early designs based on wooden frameworks were gradually pushed out of favour by the introduction of the hoop design publicised by the Lea Valley experimental station and other centres in the UK. This resulted in the term plastic 'walk-in' tunnels or 'poly-tunnels'. The last decade especially has seen many innovations, and new designs include multi-bay structures, securing methods for the polythene, and the introduction of side and roof ventilation systems.

Only comparatively recently, however, has there been any research into critical design issues, pioneered by firms such as Clovis Lande who financed a detailed study of stress factors undertaken at the National Institute of Agricultural Engineering (now the AFRC Institute of Engineering Research) at Silsoe. The information provided by the research was used to programme computers so that houses can be designed around the vital issues of wind speed and snow load, although there are obviously economic parameters to consider as no plastic structure, or for that matter greenhouse, can be designed to cope with exceptional weather unless costs are to be prohibitive.

One of the most interesting developments in the use of thin-film plastics is the process of double skinning where two skins are kept apart by a small inflation fan. This improves heat conservation to a high degree and while there is again a slight reduction in light transmission this has not proved seriously detrimental. The Serac system involves two layers of plastic in frames and claims little if any light reduction.

To summarise, therefore: gardeners wanting to use plastic structures for tomato growing can certainly do so with confidence, bearing in mind that they will have to cope with a higher humidity than they would in a greenhouse of conventional design. Many gardeners do, however, line their greenhouses with thin-film plastics for heat conservation and end up with an environment which may be very similar to that in a plastic greenhouse. It should be noted that tomatoes in full bearing must be supported, and this produces a considerable load on a plastic greenhouse, a matter which should be taken up with the supplier of the structure. *Ventilation is also a key issue, particularly in wetter districts and it would be better to put up two or three smaller plastic structures than one very large structure, so that ventilation can be effective through the ends and sides of the plastic greenhouses using side ventialtion systems,* otherwise 'ghost' spotting and botrytis may well become major problems, particularly in the autumn months. Fan ventilation can be very effective for plastic structures but fans do cost money to run. Paddle fans linked to side/end ventilation can also be highly effective. *There are now types of plastic structures with roof or ridge ventilation, which are ideal for tomatoes.*

Heat Conservation

The cost of heating greenhouses or plastic structures is such that some form of energy conservation is an important issue. There are various forms of heat conservation.

Lining the inside of greenhouses with plain or bubble polythene is one method. Bubble polythene has been shown to be the more effective of the two. Methods of securing polythene range from tacking it on to wooden astragals with a staple gun and pads of cardboard, to the use of special securing clamps with aluminium structures. Lining with polythene reduces the light transmission and, as mentioned earlier, can cause high humidity. For the early part of the season this high humidity is not detrimental and indeed can be desirable until the plants are firmly established. As the season progresses, however, the situation changes and it becomes necessary to think about effective ventilation or even removing the lining completely.

Thermal screens are another means of conserving heat. A variety of thermal screens may be used especially if the greenhouse or structure is high enough to allow a thermal screen to be pulled over above head height, as would be the case with most modern structures of commercial size. Thermal screens are used to conserve heat at night and a variety of materials may be used.

An interesting survey was made by Efford EHS (reported in *The Grower*, 10 January 1985) on the various systems of heat conservation in glasshouses and the percentage savings achieved. This is quoted below.

Methods of Heat Conservation	
Method	*Percentage Saving*
Lap sealing (sealing the glass overlaps)	5
Lining the walls of the glasshouse with polythene	6
Lining the glasshouse walls with Melinex	4.5
Removable thermal screen	27.5
Fixed thermal screen	10
Glasshouse gutter insulation	6
Full Melinex double glazing	37
Artificial windbreaks	6
Flue damper (oxygen trimming)	5.5
Computer control of glasshouse environment	5

It will be noted that this survey did not include double glazing of end or side walls with glass or polycarbonate, when savings of 5 to 10 per cent can be achieved. The cost of the methods obviously varies, but it is imperative that some heat-conservation method is written into the cost of glasshouses if crops are to be produced commercially in temperate climates.

A combination of polycarbonate or double-glazed side walls or ends with single glass in the roof and thermal screens can result in very considerable savings of heat indeed but to quantify this can be difficult in view of the variety of systems which can be used. For the average gardener lining with polythene, preferably bubble type, is likely to be the most effective, reasonably priced solution. For polythene structures double skinning, as referred to earlier, is most certainly well worth considering. It is worth commenting that, in addition to a tremendous heat saving, double-skinned structures using the inflation-fan method appear to be much more resistant to wind damage than other plastic structures.

Ventilation

It is somewhat paradoxical to talk on the one hand about heat conservation and on the other to discuss ventilation methods to cool down greenhouses or polythene structures effectively, yet the variances in solar radiation make it imperative to consider both. Excess heat can be as damaging as excess cold, and gardeners absent on business all day may be shocked to see how much temperatures can rise on a hot sunny day if one is not on hand to open doors in addition to ventilators. Many greenhouses sold to the public have very inadequate ventilation, simply because the ratio of ventilation area is not sufficiently high to allow the adequate air change necessary to keep temperatures to an acceptable level. In addition of course ventilation introduces fresh and drier air and so can reduce humidity. Ventilation tends to be rather a complicated issue dependent on a number of factors, but for smaller greenhouses there can be no doubt that side vents of the louvre or slide type, in conjunction with roof vents, will help enormously to keep a greenhouse cool during periods of high solar radiation. Lean-to structures are, as referred to earlier, notorious for building up heat unless, once again, ventilation facilities are adequate. Commercial growers should think in terms of a fully opened vent area of between 16 and 20 per cent of the floor area. Fan ventilation can be very effective in a small, inadequately ventilated greenhouse or larger commercial block in sunny, sheltered areas where there is not generally sufficient air movement to make conventional ventilation satisfactory. Ventilation of plastic structures is especially important, and has been discussed (*see above*).

GREENHOUSE ERECTION SUMMARY

Sites These should be open to avoid sun shut-off for prolonged periods. Where exposure is a problem suitable shelter should be arranged, taking into account prevailing winds and avoiding excessive sun shut-off.

Greenhouses All-glass types are ideal for both propagation and culture due to maximum light transmission in winter and summer, although they are more costly to heat during the winter–spring period when solar radiation is low. Base-wall-type houses are less costly to heat but afford poorer light transmission, although when used largely for winter–spring propagation followed by later tomato crops, this is not a great disadvantage – this is especially true of the summer period, when excess of light and solar heat can be a problem.

Ventilation The 'conventional' ventilation area (if vents are capable of being fully opened) should be at least one-fifth (20 per cent) of the floor area, and preferably operated by expansion-type vents or electric automatic systems. Fan ventilation, either extraction or pressurised, should be designed correctly with adequate fans and adequate inlet/outlet vents (*see* Chapter 2).

Ease of maintenance Aluminium alloy, galvanised or enamelled steel, superior woods or pressure-treated softwoods should be used. Glazing methods should be modern, avoiding the use of putty.

Design Easy access and adequate headroom should be considered. Sloping sides can in some cases result in reduction of headroom and crop height.

Erection This should be carried out following careful levelling and weed control. Time should be allowed for subsidence. It is essential to bring to the site a good supply of water of suitable pressure and electricity of sufficient loading.

Plastic Greenhouses

Sites The criteria are broadly similar to those for greenhouses but do be sure that exposure is taken fully into account and is not a problem necessitating the provision of shelter.

Type of structure Various forms of structure are on the market of varying widths and varying lengths. For tomato growing the newer designs, the more vertical-sided types, are likely to be much more efficient in terms of production. Crop support must be provided.

Ventilation As discussed earlier, try to keep structure lengths reasonably short when depending on end ventilation. Side ventilation is ideal. When longer or bigger structures are used, ridge or roof ventilation systems or the use of adequate extraction fans is essential if fruit spotting or botrytis is to be avoided.

Ease of maintenance Most of the steelwork involved with polythene structures is now galvanised inside and out. The life of the polythene varies but with the new 720 gauge, three years is the norm, or longer where double skinning is involved. With thinner-gauge polythene, life may be reduced, dependent on district.

Erection Polythene structures are very simple to erect if the recommended erection procedure supplied with the structures is followed. Sites should be prepared, as for greenhouses, sufficiently in advance of erection to allow for subsidence. There should also be supplies of water and electricity readily available.

2

Greenhouse Equipment

HEATING

A lot could be said about the installation of heating systems especially for tomato growing, as it is a highly specialised subject. Four main issues must be considered: (1) adequate heat level, (2) good distribution of heat, (3) precise and preferably automatic control of the heat-production system, whatever form this may take, (4) costs of fuel. It should be stressed that such considerations are for the really serious grower of tomatoes, whereas for general cultivation on a hobby basis any efficient heating system will no doubt suffice.

Maintaining Heat Levels

In calculating the heat input necessary for any building, including green-houses, the same basic procedure is followed. It must be appreciated that tomatoes do love warmth and this applies to their roots, foliage, flowers and fruit. All structural materials allow the passage of heat or cold in either direction and the rate at which this occurs depends on a number of factors, of which exposure is probably the most critical. Glass is obviously efficient in transmitting solar heat, which makes it a poor insulator. Heat loss, or as it is called technically U-value, is calculated in W/m^2 per °C or, despite metrication, more conventionally in Btu/sq ft per °F.

To calculate the heat loss of any greenhouse (or for that matter any other building) the following is the correct procedure:

1 Draw a scale plan of the greenhouse and append to this accurate meas-urements of the glass areas and of the base walls of brick or wood, where these are involved (see Fig 10).
2 Referring to the table below, calculate the heat loss per degree of temperature difference between outside and inside temperatures.
3 Now multiply by the temperature 'lift' you think will be necessary over outside temperatures. For frost protection or late tomato crops it is usual to multiply by 20, assuming that if it is 30°F (-1°C) out of doors, 50°F (10°C) will be maintained in the greenhouse. For early tomatoes, multiply by 40.
4 Now add a factor which takes into account how well constructed your greenhouse is, as an old structure with badly fitting doors and deteriorating glazing will obviously lose heat more quickly than a well-constructed, tight structure. Many gardeners find that a well-designed, wooden greenhouse is appreciably warmer than an aluminium one and that there is less con-densation, too. In very general terms it is usual to add around one-third to the final figure to take into account inadvertent heat losses. The final

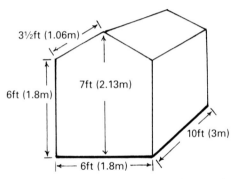

3½ft (1.06m)

7ft (2.13m)

6ft (1.8m)

10ft (3m)

6ft (1.8m)

Fig 10 Knowing your greenhouse measurements for heat loss or cubic capacity calculations

figure in watts/sq m or Btus is the quantity of heat which must be supplied by the heating system selected. This can be related to running costs.

A 2.5 kW (8530 Btus) electric heater has an output of 2,500 watts and, looking at the calculations made, it would be adequate for providing moderate heat and frost protection. The cost of running this heater can be found by relating this to the respective unit cost for electricity, taking into account the cheap rate tariff, if a 'white meter' is installed. This means making various assumptions about the level of demand on the heater. This could be very little in warmish weather or up to 50 per cent or even more during very cold weather.

Heat Losses for Various Materials		
Material	*Btu/hour per sq ft per °F*	*W/m²/°C*
Glass, including framework	1.1	6.24
4½in (12cm) brick wall or composition block	0.5	2.83
Double brick wall 9in (23cm) thick	0.4	2.27
Wood 1in (2.5cm) thick	0.5	2.83
Asbestos (sheet or corrugated)	1.1	6.24
Concrete 4in (10cm) thick	0.75	4.25
Double-glazed glass (properly sealed)	0.47	2.14
Polythene all gauges (Note saving with double skinning)	1.4 (very approx)	7.11 (very approx)

An example of how to calculate the U-value for an all-glass greenhouse (no base wall) as shown in Fig 10, is set out below.

The two sides: each 10ft (3m) x 6ft (1.8m) = 60ft² (5.4m²) x 2 = 120ft² (10.8m²)
The two ends: each 7ft (2.13m) x 6ft (1.8m) = 42ft²(3.83m²) x 2 = 84ft² (7.66m²) (including door)
And taking average height
The two sides of the roof: 10ft (3m) x 3.5ft (1.06m) = 35ft² (3.18m²) x 2 = 70ft² (6.36m²)

Total surface area = 274ft² (24.82m²)
So heat loss in Btu is 274 x 1.1 = 301Btu, or in metric terms 24.82 x 6.24
= 154W/m²/°C

Add approximately one-third for inadvertent heat losses. Taking this into
account, figures now become:

$301 + \frac{1}{3} = 400$Btu (approx),
or in metric terms $154 + \frac{1}{3} = 200$W/m²/°C (approx).

The next stage is to multiply these figures by the estimated 'lift' over outside
temperatures.

Degrees F	*Degrees C*
20° lift (400x20)=8,000Btu (2.3kW)	11° lift (200x11)=2,200W/m²/°C (2.2kW)
30° lift (400x30)=1,200Btu (3.5kW)	17° lift (200x17)=3,400W/m°/°C (3.4kW)
40° lift (400x40)=1,600Btu (4.6kW)	23° lift (200x23)=4,600W/m²/°C (4.6kW)

Note that figures are rounded off for convenience.

Assuming however that there is a 50 per cent demand, the cost over 24 hours
would be 50 per cent of 24 x 2,500 = 3,000. A kilowatt (1,000 watts) is the
unit used for costing purposes so that the cost of running the heater for 24
hours would be 30 units at the appropriate tariff. Where other methods of
heat distribution are used, such as hot water piping it is a question of referring to tables for the output of heat per 1ft (30cm) of the pipe of the chosen
diameter. This can be seen by referring to the table.

An important consideration is in which period of the year the minimum

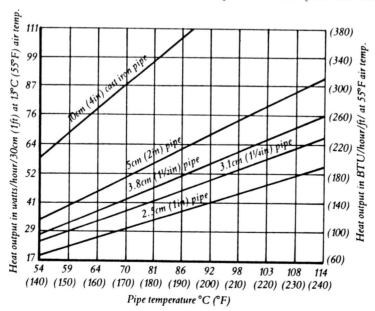

temperatures will be required. If, for example, winter propagation followed by tomato planting in February is desired, due allowance must be made for coping with outside temperatures of a very low order (possibly 15°F/9°C). Taking this into consideration it can be seen that a temperature 'lift' of about 40°F (23°C) over outside temperatures must be allowed. This means multiplying the heat-loss figure by 40 (23). For tomatoes planted in April or May even a 10°F (5.6°C) lift may be acceptable, much of course depending on the region of Britain, level of exposure and so on.

With cold culture no heating is of course involved, although experience shows that in the northern part of Britain completely cold culture of tomatoes can result in a very late crop and raises problems of excess humidity – with its disease implications.

For commercial-sized greenhouses, it is necessary to make far more detailed calculations, taking into account: (1) location and the degree days for the area concerned, (2) whether a block or part of a block of greenhouses/structures is concerned, (3) whether single- or double-glazed, (4) precise heat levels demanded and when, (5) other associated factors such as levels of exposure, use of thermal screens etc.

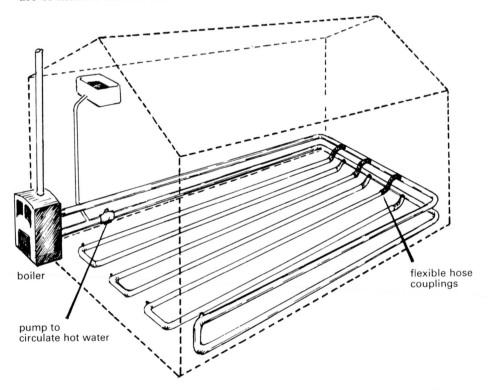

boiler

flexible hose couplings

pump to circulate hot water

Fig 11 Ideal pipe layout for a larger-scale tomato house using flexible hose couplings to bring pipe loops to ground level between rows. Grooved polystyrene slabs can be placed on top of pipes for growbag, NFT or perlite systems

Distribution of Heat

Heat is provided by radiation and by convection, and invariably a combination of both. Radiation heat, which is directional, will be given off by warm pipes, but convection currents will also be developed as the air warmed by radiation in the vicinity of the pipes rises, setting up convection air movement.

Non-fan, convector electric heaters operate in a similar fashion by warming air which discharges itself and sets up convection currents, whereas fan-type heaters blow the warm air out in a specific direction, but here again convection currents are also developed. Free-discharge heat from a central source in a greenhouse, is obviously not as efficient as heat properly distributed, simply because cold curtains of air quickly develop due to the rapid heat loss through the glass. Different air movement on the outside of the greenhouse can also encourage the development of these cold areas. Warm-air heating systems can only be considered totally efficient when the air is distributed through polythene ducts, but it should be explained that such efficiency is only really of importance for early crops when outside temperatures are likely to be low.

So far we have only considered warming the air, but of course it is highly important for tomato culture that the soil or growing medium is sufficiently warm – not below 56–7°F (about 13°C) at 4–6in (10–15cm) depths. It can

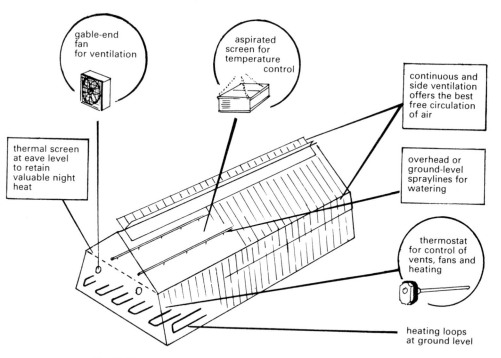

Fig 12 Features valuable in controlling the greenhouse environment

be seen therefore that there are considerable difficulties in achieving this soil warmth uniformly when relying entirely on non-directional warm-air systems, and the same may be said of badly designed pipe systems.

The ideal warm-pipe system for tomato growing is one designed on the small-bore principle, using $1^{1}/_{4}$–2in (3.1–5cm) diameter pipes. These small-diameter pipes, containing as they do only one-fifth of the volume of water of an old-fashioned 4in (10cm) system of similar heat capacity, can be readily spread across the growing area between the plants, and on the soil if necessary, which they warm by radiation heat. In addition they are, by virtue of the smaller volume of water, able to respond to the need for heat much more quickly than a 4in (10cm) system with its large bulk of water, and this is important for tomato growing where precise temperature control is desirable. Note also that if rubber hose combined with expanding clips is used for the joints of the interspersed pipes, this allows them to be left on the soil for soil warming by radiation and conduction early in the year and lifted up a few inches thereafter to give convection heat. Where long lengths of small-bore pipes are used, a circulating pump is necessary, and here lies the main advantage of large-bore systems (3–4in or 7.5–10cm), in which the water circulates quite readily by gravity, provided there is a gradual rise from the boiler to the highest point and a gradual fall back thereafter. Large-scale systems are installed according to precise design criteria, but a typical pipe layout for a small commercial glasshouse is as shown in Fig 11.

Heating Methods and Costs

Types of heating for tomatoes or greenhouses generally need not of course rely on small- or large-bore water-filled pipe systems. The following is a summary of heating methods:

1 Water-containing pipes – boiler fired with solid fuel, oil, gas or electricity. Simple types are not automatic. More refined types are semi-automatic. Refined oil, gas or electric boilers are completely automatic. There is interest in the late 1980s in using straw, wood or municipal waste pellets.
2 Oil heaters – free discharge or ducted, heated air. These can be with or without pressure jet, vaporiser burners, or assisted air discharge by means of fans. Simple types are controlled manually, other types operate on a thermostat.
3 Various forms of electrical apparatus – all reasonably automatic:
   a Soil- or bench-warming cables (see p37), which have little effect on air temperature
   b Mineral-insulated (MI) cables fitted around the greenhouse perimeter (not considered ideal for tomatoes)
   c Tubular heaters, generally fitted on perimeter walls
   d Fan heaters, which are generally free standing in the centre of the greenhouse, but there is a larger type which can be sited at one end of the house (ideally these should be controlled by a separate thermostat)

e Storage heaters – there are some problems with these owing to lack of temperature control

f Infra-red heaters located above the crop

g Radiant gas heaters are also used for greenhouse heating

The approximate cost of operating the various heating systems can be calculated from the fuel-cost table in Appendix 1.

It is obvious that for full-level heating, solid-fuel and oil-fired systems are much more economic to run that electrical systems, but on the other hand they are generally much more expensive to install, and they frequently offer considerable control problems compared with electrical heating units which are simple to control thermostatically, a matter which will be discussed further.

Note also the lower cost of 'off peak' electricity (*see* Appendix 1 comparison of fuel costs).

Ventilation

While much has been said about the tomato plant's need for warmth, it must also be stressed that tomatoes dislike excess heat and very high humidity. Excess heat, apart from causing wilting and scorching, can lower fruit quality. Reducing the temperature of a greenhouse when either solar heat or artificial heat (generally residual), or both, has raised the temperature above a desirable level can be effected in three ways:

1 The warm or lighter air is allowed to escape through suitably large ventilators set in the highest part of the structure, and is replaced by cooler outside air by reciprocal interchange or inadvertently by entry through leaks in glass overlaps or joins, the edge of doors, or ideally by lower-set

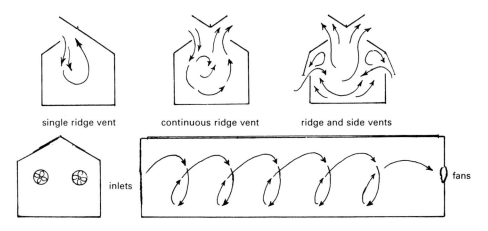

single ridge vent   continuous ridge vent   ridge and side vents

inlets   fans

gable-end fans with gable inlet vents give the best air circulation

Fig 13 The air circulation provided by different ventilation systems

vents. The correct ventilator size, when the vents are capable of opening fully, is one-fifth of the floor area of the greenhouse. The ventilators can be operated manually or by electrical systems which are thermostatically controlled, or better still and at lower cost, they can be expansion-type vents which operate at pre-set temperatures.

2 Extractor-type fans extract the warm air and pull in cooler air through inlets, vents or louvres of suitable size. The fans operate thermostatically and, if necessary, the inlets too can be operated automatically – but this is generally done manually in small greenhouses.

3 'Pressurised' systems are installed whereby fans push air into the house, and the warmer air escapes through counterbalanced louvres.

Each system has its virtues and failings. Conventional ventilating systems depend much on the movement of outside air, whereas fan systems operate more or less independently of outside air movement and are much more effective in achieving the required number of complete air changes (generally 40 to 50 per hour), to reduce the temperature of the greenhouse efficiently. Fan ventilation systems do cost money to operate, however, and although the amount of electricity power they consume is small, some gardeners and growers seem to begrudge it. Breakdown of fans or power failure can be a problem, although where this occurs with the smaller greenhouses the inlet vent coupled with open doors can usually cope for limited periods.

Pressurised systems can result in temperature gradients developing throughout the greenhouse due to localised pressure buildup, but in practice such gradients are small enough to be disregarded.

To summarise, most smaller greenhouses will depend on a mixture of manual vents and expansion vents. Only the more intensive growers will consider investment in more sophisticated systems.

Controlling Heat Input

There are various methods of controlling the generation of heat in a greenhouse, whether this involves the use of a switch to allow input or cessation of electric power, or the means of igniting or extinguishing a boiler. Obviously the efficiency achieved will vary according to the sophistication of the equipment. For example, a pressure-jet, oil-fired boiler can be fully automatic, whereas an oil burner may only be partly automatic, alternating between the pre-set heat and pilot heat.

A very common way of achieving automatic control with hot-water systems where circulation depends completely on a circulating pump is to control the pump operation thermostatically. An alternative to this would be the use of solenoid valves.

Thermostats and other instruments, to be fully effective in a greenhouse, should preferably be aspirated, so that a small fan draws a constant flow of air typical of that in the greenhouse over the controlling instruments. If sited openly all instruments tend to record atypical temperatures or conditions due to the buildup of solar radiation, the effects of draughts, or radiation losses. This applies to thermometers also. In recent years the use of electronic sensors has become popular, it being claimed that these are much less affected by outside influences, something which is borne out in practice. Obviously there are limits to the degree of sophistication which can be readily afforded, yet it has been shown that accurate control of heating systems and ventilation results in a much more even temperature regime, with highly advantageous results to crop performance and fuel consumption.

Equipment is now available for the achievement of almost complete environmental control in greenhouses, including control of temperature and humidity patterns compatible with preceding and prevailing light levels, and such equipment is now relatively commonplace in many modern commercial glasshouse establishments. Further information on glasshouse environmental control equipment is available from specialist suppliers (*see* Fig 12).

WATERING AND FEEDING

In addition to greenhouses and their heating systems, there are certain other requirements for succesful tomato culture, particularly when there is a desire to reduce labour by the use of automatic or semi-automatic equipment. Watering and feeding are undoubtedly the two most important issues, and it is difficult to divorce them. Many of the more modern systems of culture such as growbags more or less demand accurate placement of water although it is true that all systems of culture will benefit from good watering systems.

Water Supply

Much depends on the size of the greenhouse unit in deciding what constitutes an adequate water supply. Large areas of greenhouse require a sufficient volume and pressure of water in order to operate the spray-lines – now an essential part of commercial equipment – and this means that a mains-supply pipe of fairly large diameter must be laid directly to the greenhouse. Many water authorities, however, now insist on the installation of a special reservoir tank, usually butyl-lined corrugated iron or something similar, with an electric pump to provide the outflow, and they do this not only in the interests of the grower, but because of the liquid fertilisers which may find their way back into the mains supply where there is a direct takeoff from the main.

Amateur gardeners, however, should seldom run into these complications, and usually a supply pipe of $1/2$–1in (1.25–2.5cm) diameter can be installed, either in permanent underground form with water authority permission (and possibly an extra charge) or linked to an outside tap and detached when not in use. Such systems need to allow complete drain-off during the winter and are therefore not always suitable for year-round use, unless well insulated, and even then there is a risk factor with frost.

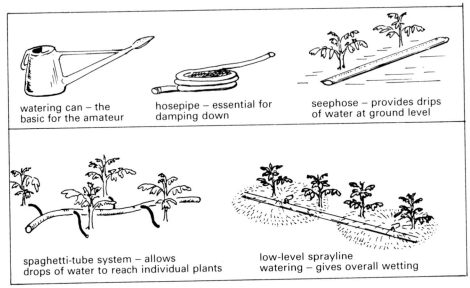

Fig 14 The different watering systems

Watering Systems

Sprinkler systems Sprinklers providing large droplets of water and intended mainly for the damping-down essential to pollination are fitted at a height of approximately 6–7ft (2m) and, whilst in frequent use commercially, are as yet seldom used by amateurs.

Spraylines These, like sprinklers, are fitted overhead for the early part of the season at about 6–7ft (2m) and then, if desired, inverted and dropped to about 1ft (30cm) later in the season when the lower fruit trusses are removed. They provide water in fine mist form and are capable of watering the whole growing area. They are not highly suitable for container systems as the water is prevented from entering the container by the foliage of the plant. Good pressure and volume of water are required for the successful operation of spraylines, a matter for precise specification.

Trickle systems These involve the precise placement of water, in droplet form to avoid soil structure damage, adjacent to the plant and are therefore ideally suited to container growing systems. In certain types of light soil the water tends to form a cylindrical column and restricts root development. Very popular now are 'spaghetti' systems of drip watering.

Low-level sprinkler systems These can involve 'lie-flat' polythene where 2in (5.6cm) wide perforated polythene tubing expands when filled with water and sends out fine jets of moisture. Rigid PVC or plastic bi-wall or 'leaky' hosepipe bored with small holes operates in a similar way. A fair pressure and volume of water are needed for the successful operation of these systems, which are satisfactory for border or trough culture, although 'leaky' hose is best used for sub-irrigation.

Hosepipes The most common method of watering for the amateur is with a hosepipe, either open ended or fitted with a rose. Damage to soil structure can, however, easily occur by continuous and careless use of open-ended hoses, apart from which holding hoses can be a time-consuming method of watering. Damping-down is frequently carried out with a hosepipe, either by pinching in the end of the hose or using a spray nozzle. Hosepipe watering is satisfactory for both border and container growing, provided the pressure is reduced to the minimum compatible with sufficient outlet and is carried out at the right times.

Watering cans and internal reservoirs The gardener who grows only a few plants relies frequently on a can, replenishing it from a tank or container that is kept filled. There is some virtue in this method, as it allows bulk mixing of liquid fertilisers, but obviously can-watering is laborious work and it is much more suitable for container growing systems than for border culture. Hygiene is an important issue when tanks and tubs are used to store water, as these can frequently become contaminated with algae and disease. Apart from this the dilution rate of liquid feeds tends to vary as the tanks are seldom completely emptied before being replenished.

Dilution of Liquid Fertilisers

The use of fertilisers in liquid form is almost essential for container growing systems, and while the small-scale bulk mixing referred to above may be acceptable for small-scale culture, it would be completely unsuitable for large-scale growing. Diluters are devices into which the 'stock', or concentrated solution of the liquid fertiliser, is put. Adjustment is usually possible so that a specific dilution can be achieved, although in practice some diluters, due to various factors such as differing water pressures, tend to be erratic in behaviour or cannot be linked to mains supplies. All liquid fertilisers must be accurately measured and diluted, otherwise plants can be damaged. For large scale NFT or rockwool systems very sophisticated control equipment is required.

Carbon Dioxide Enrichment

The technique of artificially enriching the atmosphere with additional carbon dioxide (CO_2) has received considerable publicity in recent years, especially in the realms of early cropping. It has been shown in many cases to have a highly beneficial effect on size and quality of lower fruit trusses by increasing the speed of photosynthesis. The natural complement of CO_2 in the atmosphere is 300 parts per million (300vpm) and it is usual to give three-fold enrichment, ie to 1,000vpm, during daylight hours, from half an hour after sunrise till one hour before sunset. Carbon dioxide can be provided: (1) by burning paraffin, though this can give rise to sulphur fumes; the use of flueless oil stoves for heating purposes does in fact provide considerable CO_2; (2) by the burning of propane or natural gas in special burners; (3) by the use of 'dry ice'; (4) by the use of liquid CO_2 dispersed from a tank through perforated polythene tubes.

The requirement for CO_2 is in the region of 100–130lb (approximately 50kg) per 1,000sq ft (830m²) for the propagation period, and 700–800lb (approximately 340kg) per 1,000 sq ft (830m²) for the growing period. Obviously there will be a varying requirement according to the level of ventilation demanded by solar radiation, as CO_2 enrichment will not proceed simultaneously with ventilation.

One of the problems with CO_2 enrichment is the correct measurement of its level, and this demands specialised checking equipment. Owing to the degree of precision necessary, it is unlikely that many amateur gardeners will purposely set out to provide extra CO_2 although those wishing to do so can certainly obtain the necessary information from fuel-supplying bodies and advisory services. The culture of tomatoes under straw-bale systems results in considerable CO_2 supplementation from the decomposing straw. Probably the same is true of organic growing methods.

ADDITIONAL EQUIPMENT
Benches and Bench Warming

Benches are a very necessary part of tomato culture when plants are self raised. Open benches, made or bought, of superior pressure-treated or painted wood slats, are built at a height of 30in (75cm) and are ideal for tomato raising, especially if there is a pipe heating system some 9–12in (23–30cm) below the bench. Heat can readily pass through the bench and between the plants.

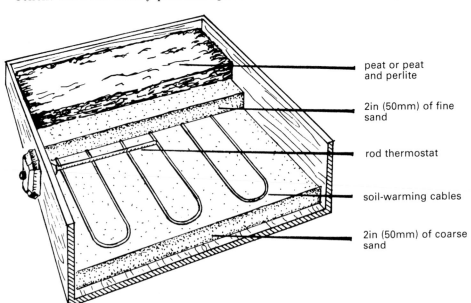

peat or peat and perlite

2in (50mm) of fine sand

rod thermostat

soil-warming cables

2in (50mm) of coarse sand

Fig 15 A home-made propagation bench using electrical soil-warming cables

3 One of the earlier types of growing rooms with pegboard sides and spray lines. While designs have changed, the technique of using fluorescent tubes is still highly effective for plant raising

Solid benches constructed of asbestos or corrugated iron, with a layer of ashes, peat or sand are however frequently used in the interests of reducing watering and, provided that there is a space between the bench and the outside of the greenhouse to allow the passage of heat, they cannot be seriously faulted. Angle steel and aluminium components are excellent for bench construction, especially if used with expanded metal or mesh sheets.

For tomato propagation on a smaller scale there is much to be said for the provision of warming cables, either mains voltage or low voltage, set in a 4–5in (10–12.5cm) layer of sand. The use of a purpose-made or modified propagating case, or even a polythene tent, over a warmed bench would commend itself to the small-scale grower wishing to provide the necessary propagating temperature for tomatoes at a lower cost, as the air temperature of the greenhouse can then be considerably reduced.

Specifications for bench warming Use a solid bench of corrugated iron or asbestos with 6in (15cm) sides. Fine sand should be laid to a 2in (5cm) depth and mains voltage cable laid lengthwise at 2–4in (5–10cm) intervals to give a loading of 8–12 watts per square foot (86–130W/m²). A 2in (5cm) layer of sand is placed over the cable. Control is by an 18in (45cm) rod or phial and capillary-tube thermostat, across the run of the wire just below the surface of the bench. Use peat between the boxes or pots to cover the

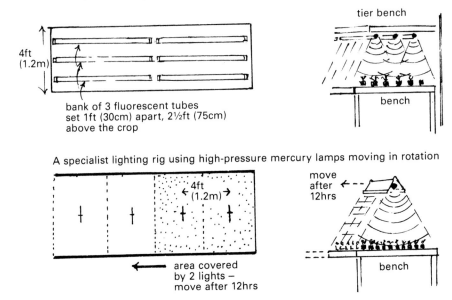

Simple bench rig for the amateur using fluorescent tubes 8ft (2.4m) long

4ft (1.2m)

bank of 3 fluorescent tubes
set 1ft (30cm) apart, 2½ft (75cm)
above the crop

tier bench

bench

A specialist lighting rig using high-pressure mercury lamps moving in rotation

4ft (1.2m)

area covered
by 2 lights –
move after 12hrs

move
after
12hrs

bench

Fig 16 Lighting rigs for growing seedlings from pricking off to planting

bench and prevent needless heat loss. Warm water pipes laid in grooves in polystyrene, electric foil or hot box propagators are now more popular for general propagation activities.

Growing Rooms

Tomato plants are frequently raised commercially in specially constructed growing rooms where high light levels are provided, temperature being controlled by fans and heaters. The heat from the lights in most instances is sufficient to maintain the temperature of the room, except during very cold weather. Seedlings, after germination in a germinating cabinet or greenhouse, are pricked off into small pots and then placed in the growing room for light treatment.

Specifications for growing rooms This is a specialised matter best taken up with the appropriate electricity board (*see Electric Growing* published by the Electricity Council; *see also* Chapter 5). Temperatures are 74.5°F (23.5°C) 'day' (12 hours) and 63°F (17°C) 'night' for 14–21 days according to light levels, which should ideally be around 10,000 1x, or half this light level on a static rig with a 16-hour 'day'.

Lighting

Apart from a working light provided by tungsten filament lamps, which would be essential for the enthusiastic grower, there is increasing interest in the use of supplementary lighting for tomato growing, especially for early cropping, in order to speed up photosynthesis in the young tomato plant and particularly during poor light periods. This technique is by no means new but has been the subject of some controversy for a great many years and recommendations have recently been somewhat modified.

Specification for supplementary lighting HLRG mercury fluorescent reflector lamps 2.5ft (75cm) above bench, 4ft (1.2m) apart. Alternatively MBFR/U lamps suspended 3ft (90cm) above bench 4ft (1.2m) apart can be used. Both types of lamp can either be permanently fixed or on a sliding rail to allow batch treatment. Either type will cover 200 seedlings. Fluorescent tubes can also be used, and have been proved to be as efficient. The lighting period should not be in excess of 16 hours in each 24, the plants having 8 hours' darkness, over a period of 14–21 days (*see also* Chapter 5). The greenhouse temperature should be 68°F (20°C) by day and 60°F (16°C) at night.

Of considerable interest is the use of tungsten filament such as in Sungro-lites, which are ideal for low-cost treatment of seedlings especially at the post-germination stages.

Capillary Benches

These provide for a constant supply of water $\frac{1}{2}$in (1.25cm) below the surface of coarse sand, which is spread out in a 2–3in (5–7.5cm) layer in a perfectly flat polythene-lined 'basin', the water level being controlled by a ball-cock tank set alongside the bench or a float controller. Such benches are used mostly for growing rooms.

Lining for Greenhouses

The lining of greenhouses with light-gauge polythene is a useful technique for reducing heat loss (*see also* p22). Polythene or bubble lining cannot be compared with double glazing, where two hermetically sealed panes of glass provide a 'dead' layer of air between them. It does, however, considerably

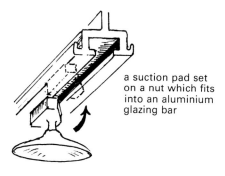

a suction pad set on a nut which fits into an aluminium glazing bar

lining the inside of a small aluminium greenhouse with polythene will save 10–25 per cent of your heat cost in winter

Fig 17 Lining a small greenhouse with polythene

reduce the heat loss through overlaps in the glass or loose glazing systems and at the same time prevents draughts. The quoted reduction in heat loss is approximately 10–25 per cent.

Lining with polythene is usually carried out only partially, leaving vents so that they can be opened fully. A raising of the humidity occurs due to condensation on the polythene and this, while advantageous for propagation, can be slightly disadvantageous for full-season growing. For this reason polythene lining is perhaps best employed only on a limited scale for tomato growing, preferably along a side subjected to cold winds or in the region of doors, or as a night-time thermal screen.

Specification for lining Light-gauge or bubble polythene is tacked on with drawing-pins or staples through paper pads, to astragals or wooden strips fitted into the space that frequently exists between the extruded alloy glazing bars. Vents and doors, if left unobstructed, can be fitted with movable curtains of polythene. Alternatively, special fixing clips are now available to make things a lot simpler.

Thermal Screens

The installation and operation of these is best taken up with a specialist supplier.

Computers for Environmental Control

These are available now at reasonable cost and will give detailed records of air temperatures night and day, of the effectiveness of a heating system, of ventilation levels, CO_2 enrichment and the effect of thermal screens, for the control of irrigation, and for many other facets of growth.

Floor Liners

It is now standard practice to spread white polythene on the floor of the greenhouse to reflect light and for general hygiene (or use black/white polythene, white-side uppermost).

3

The Physiology of the
Tomato Plant

THE GENERAL PHYSIOLOGICAL ASPECTS OF GROWTH

All green plants depend on supplies of air, moisture and nutrients, and thereafter, if there are no inhibiting factors, growth proceeds at a temperature and light level suited to the metabolism of the plant in question. It has been agreed that the particular metabolism of the tomato plant demands constant warmth and a high light intensity, and the gardener or grower must therefore provide these conditions; at the same time attention must be paid to the tomato's gross appetite for essential elements.

Breeding programmes for new varieties of tomatoes have in recent years tended to concentrate on producing varieties suited to a specific range of environmental conditions, even to the extent of 'sub-arctic' varieties which it is claimed grow and produce fruit under much cooler conditions than conventional varieties.

The complexities surrounding growth are discussed fully in works on botany or plant physiology, but it will perhaps help us to understand the physiology of tomatoes better if some of the more important general issues are briefly referred to.

Respiration

The function of breathing is carried on by all living organisms. Air is taken in through the pores of green plant leaves, and to a lesser extent the stems, the oxygen content in the air is extracted as energy for various chemical processes and the carbon dioxide is expelled. The rate at which respiration takes place depends on the age of the plant – a young plant breathes faster than an old plant – the temperature, and of course the rate of growth. Respiration is, however, a katabolic (destructive) and continuous process, night and day, an important thing to remember in tomato growing with respect to day and night temperatures and the using up at night of carbohydrate manufactured during the day. This is the reason why there can be excessive curling of leaves, a matter which is discussed more fully later.

Process of respiration This is carried on continuously, as follows:

Air – oxygen extracted for energy and various chemical processes – carbon dioxide expelled

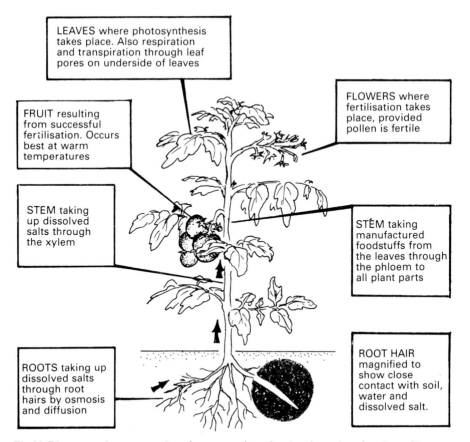

LEAVES where photosynthesis takes place. Also respiration and transpiration through leaf pores on underside of leaves

FRUIT resulting from successful fertilisation. Occurs best at warm temperatures

STEM taking up dissolved salts through the xylem

FLOWERS where fertilisation takes place, provided pollen is fertile

STĒM taking manufactured foodstuffs from the leaves through the phloem to all plant parts

ROOTS taking up dissolved salts through root hairs by osmosis and diffusion

ROOT HAIR magnified to show close contact with soil, water and dissolved salt.

Fig 18 Diagrammatic representation of a tomato plant showing the various functions of its parts

Photosynthesis

During photosynthesis air is taken in by the plant through its pores, the carbon dioxide contained in it at 300 parts per million (or more) is extracted and the oxygen is expelled – the direct antithesis of respiration. Photosynthesis takes place only in the presence of light and with the aid of the catalyst chlorophyll, the green pigment present in all green plants. As photosynthesis is responsible for the formation of the carbohydrates essential to sustain growth, there is a direct relationship between the rate of photosynthesis and the rate of growth, including the swelling of fruit. The speed at which photosynthesis takes place in the presence of adequate water, carbon dioxide and nutrients depends largely on temperature and light levels.

Modern research suggests, however, that there are times when there is insufficient carbon dioxide present in the air to allow photosynthesis to take place rapidly enough to cope with the requirements of the plant. The research work carried out with carbon dioxide has given some spectacular results in many cases, resulting in larger and earlier yields of high-quality fruit. Generally speaking, all specialist early tomato growers will now practise

CO_2 enrichment in one or other of its forms. While it is not a process likely to be deliberately taken up by smaller-scale growers or domestic gardeners, the use of oil or gas heating in flueless forms, or the straw-bale technique of growing, adds considerably to the natural complement of CO_2. Note, however, there can be a detrimental effect on growth should toxic fumes develop from oil-burning appliances, so care is necessary.

Process of photosynthesis This proceeds only in the presence of light and its rate is governed by light and temperature levels. The process is as follows:

Air – carbon dioxide extracted – oxygen expelled

Transpiration

Water absorbed by the roots (*see* 'Osmosis' below) rises up through the stem, being passed from cell to cell through tissue called the xylem, and travels into the leaves. Water that is superfluous to the needs of the plant is expelled as water vapour through the pores in the stem and leaves, the evaporation process allowing the plant to keep 'cool'. Simultaneously, a transpiration stream is created, capable of transporting dissolved nutrients through the plant.

It is essential for the tomato grower to appreciate that the rate of water uptake (and nutrients in solution) is dependent on: (1) the state of the roots, (2) the health and condition of the xylem tissue of the plant, (3) the total leaf area of the plant, (4) other related factors such as the general condition of

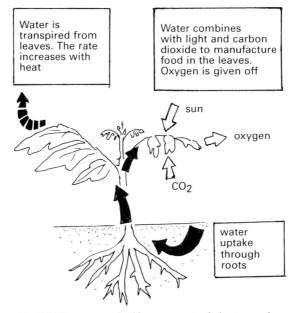

Fig 19 Water – a valuable component of plant growth

plant tissue other than the xylem (*see* 'Osmosis' below). When the transpiration rate is excessive such as in a hot dry atmosphere, and especially when there is a large amount of foliage, the plant cells partially collapse, normally recovering at night when it is cooler and the rate of transpiration slows up. This is especially the case when the temperature suddenly rises, following a relatively cool period of several days. The rate of uptake also depends: (5) on the temperature of the air, (6) the humidity of the atmosphere (the rate of water vapour discharge is directly related to the humidity of the air and the respective pressures inside and outside the plant), and (7), perhaps most important of all, on the respective osmotic pressures in the soil and the plant (*see* 'Osmosis' below).

Process of transpiration Water is taken into the plant through the process of osmosis, passed up to the leaves, and a proportion is given off as water vapour at a rate dependent largely on temperature, humidity, and the respective osmotic pressures of plant and soil.

Osmosis

This important process is one which must be fully understood by tomato growers, particularly those concerned with the more sophisticated forms of culture now practised, especially where these are concerned with limited quantities of growing media or nutrient solutions (*see* Chapter 6).

Osmosis is a process whereby a high concentration of salts in solution on one side of a semi-permeable membrane absorbs the water of a less concentrated solution through the semi-permeable membrane. The cell wall of a plant is a typical semi-permeable membrane. In simpler terms, the stronger concentration in the cell of the root of the plant 'pulls' on the less concentrated solution contained in the soil through the semi-permeable cell wall. Note that, technically speaking, osmosis only pulls in the water, it being stated by plant physiologists that the solution of nutrients enters the plant by diffusion, a separate process though closely associated with osmosis.

The movement of the solution from cell to cell in the plant through the cell walls goes on by an osmotic chain reaction, the cell which has received water having its salt concentration lowered, thus allowing the now more concentrated solution in the next cell to pull in its solution, and so on.

The rate at which the uptake of water and nutrients takes place, while partly dependent on the rate of transpiration, also hinges largely on the ability of the plant to take in water initially by osmosis. Obviously if there is near equilibrium between the soil and the root, for example when the salt solution of the soil, growing medium or solution is altered by the application of concentrated fertilisers (liquid or solid), the plant will be unable to absorb freely. Indeed, if excess fertiliser is applied, reverse osmosis may take place, causing serious damage to plant tissue, this being the way in which some weedkillers act.

By exercising strict control over the concentration of liquid fertilisers applied to the soil or growing media, it is possible to exert a marked influence in the growth rate of the plant. Where there is no soil but instead peat, perlite, rockwool or nutrient solution, the same general principles will apply. This is of considerable importance for the culture of early tomatoes, which often tend to make vegetative instead of productive growth, especially when light levels are low.

Process of osmosis The stronger salt solution of plant cell, ie in the root hair, 'pulls' in the weaker solution from the soil and there is a chain reaction throughout the plant. Control of soil solution can exercise in turn a considerable control over the growth rate of the plant.

Translocation

This is the movement of the salts and manufactured foodstuffs around the plant, largely through tissue known as phloem. Foods manufactured in the leaves are obviously required for various functions throughout the plant tissue, particularly for the swelling of the fruit. Irregularities in watering, temperature or ventilation can disrupt the transport of foodstuffs, resulting in various troubles such as uneven fruit ripening, 'blackbottoms' on fruit, leaf distortions and many other symptoms (*see* Chapter 11). Unbalanced nutritional conditions are usually highly contributory to the various irregularities.

Pollination and Fertilisation

The sexual reproduction process carried out by all flowering plants depends on the male pollen grain reaching the stigma of the female (pollination), the subsequent germination of the pollen grain and the growth of a pollen tube so that fusion between the male gamete and the female ovule takes place (fertilisation). The flowers of the tomato plant, which contain both male and female organs, are so shaped that self-pollination readily occurs although some assistance is welcomed. Tapping with a cane or shaking by applying droplets of water helps considerably. A reasonably humid atmosphere will also ensure that the pollen grain does not dry out before it germinates, this being the main reason why damping-down is practised so frequently. Partial or complete failure of fertilisation is due to various causes, including infertile pollen, and will result in small 'chat' fruits or the complete dropping of the flower by shrivelling of the stalk, due to lack of the necessary stimulus from fertilisation. Fertile pollen is best produced when there is a sufficiently high light intensity during truss initiation, and when temperature and level of nutrients have been satisfactory. These matters will be referred to in more detail in Chapter 5 and elsewhere.

PLANT NUTRIENTS AND THE TOMATO

Plant nutrition is a very complicated and involved subject, and to discuss it in detail is beyond the scope of this book. I have alluded briefly to the methods by which the green growing plant obtains its nutrients – by osmosis, gaseous

exchange and diffusion – and these processes are basic to all plant growth. Some elementary understanding of plant nutrition is, however, essential if one is to exercise any control over the rate and precise manner in which the plant grows and to coax it to produce the maximum amount of fruit – and this is particularly so with tomatoes.

Organic Growing

The current interest in organic growing avoiding the use of inorganic syn-thesised chemicals, as opposed to those of 'natural' derivation from compost or other natural sources, does not alter the needs of the growing plant for basic chemicals, no matter what their source may be. Organic growers do, however, endeavour by following 'natural' systems of growing to produce more balanced plant growth which they claim has greater resistance to pest and disease attack. Perhaps more importantly the end product which in this case is the tomato fruit, will be of better quality.

What are Plant Nutrients?

Essential elements are required by all living organisms to provide the energy needed for all the various processes concerned with growth. We devour our food, but the plant is not able to digest solid elements; it can only take them when they are either dissolved in water, which itself contains essential elements (oxygen and hydrogen), or in the form of a gas, in the case of carbon and oxygen.

Once dissolved, these elements can be taken in either by the roots of the plant or absorbed through the leaves, provided the chemicals are not of a form which would cause physical damage to the leaves.

Nutrients from the Soil

All soils are derived from the long-term weathering of the rocks which form the crust of the earth. Over the course of a great many years what is known as the soil has developed on the surface of the earth. It contains a heterogeneous collection of broken-down rock, the particle size of which varies from gravel through sand, silt and clay. Intermingled with the mineral particles are plant and animal remains and a vast population of micro-organisms and larger forms of life such as worms, all with differing roles.

The precise nature of a soil is classified largely by the particle size: 'light' sandy soils are composed predominantly of larger particles; 'heavy' clay soils of small particles; and 'medium' soils of a mixture of both. Beneficial bacteria generally thrive well in well-aerated soils and carry on their various roles of rendering nutrients palatable to plants; for example proteins are reduced to nitrogen. The process of rendering nutrients soluble causes intense chemical

4 Pollination is a key issue – and the movement of the pollen from anthers to stigma can be assisted by tapping the flower trusses lightly with a cane or alternatively by using a vibrator (home-made types are often made with electric bells)

activity largely through the acids formed by bacterial and chemical action. Much of this process takes place on the large surface area of the mineral particles, and it is therefore desirable to build up crumb structure in the soil, so that the fine particles adhere together. This is achieved through the formation of organic gums, which arise from the activities of micro-organisms; electrolytic action also brings sub-particles together.

The constituents of rocks vary considerably throughout the world, but to our knowledge invariably include silicon, aluminium, phosphorus, potassium, calcium, magnesium, sulphur, boron, manganese, copper, zinc, iron, molybdenum, chlorine, sodium, iodine, cobalt and selenium. Other elements essential for plant growth are hydrogen and oxygen, which are 90 to 95 per cent supplied by water, and nitrogen derived from the atmosphere by fixation and precipitation, and of course by the breakdown of organic matter. Carbon is also essential, this largely being taken up in gaseous form from the atmosphere.

Where soils are used for the culture of tomatoes, there will already be a limited natural source of elements and plant nutrients available to the plants. Where soil-less mediums are used, nearly all the nutrients must be supplied artificially in palatable form by the addition of readily soluble fertilisers, and this is a matter which will be discussed further in Chapter 4.

Other Sources of Nutrients

With the current emphasis on producing crops, including tomatoes, in soil-less systems, it is important to appreciate that the chemicals necessary for plant growth are available from a very wide range of sources. With organic growing systems the main sources will be from the decomposition of various plant material which ideally has been grown organically in the first place before being naturally composted, thus avoiding the use of synthesised inorganic chemicals in the composting process. In addition, there is a vast range of organic material which provides nutrients, such as seaweed, fish meal, dried blood, hoof and horn meal, wood ash, sewage sludge and of course certain indispensable inorganic chemicals naturally occurring such as ground limestone, rock phosphates and rock potash. It is also important to appreciate, however, that at the end of the day, and whatever source is involved, the plant assimilates simple chemicals.

The Types and Function of Nutrients

When discussing plant nutrition and the precise role of each element in the general metabolism of the plant, it is easy to fall into the trap of thinking, in compartmentalised fashion, that one element is responsible for only one function. Such is certainly not the case, as the whole process of growth is a most complicated and interrelated chemical process involving integration over the whole range of elements which are necessary for successful growth, but obviously in quantities which vary between different species of plants.

The only practical way of discussing plant nutrition is, however, to give

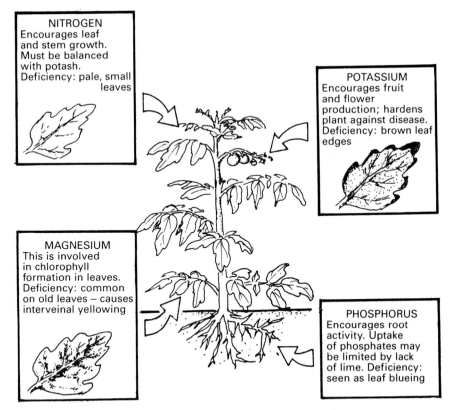

Fig 20 The major elements required by tomatoes

more or less individual consideration to the elements concerned, and this we shall now do with particular reference to tomato culture (*see also* Chapter 4). But it must be remembered that each and every element is a cog in the wheel of growth and that if one is missing a breakdown in growth can occur.

Nitrogen (N) Nitrogen is present in all forms of animal and plant material capable of life, and nitrogen is therefore contained in animal and plant micro- and macro-organism remains. The sphere of growth where nitrogen appears to play the largest part is by overall increase of total bulk. With tomato plants an excess of nitrogen can be an embarrassment by inducing soft and relatively unproductive growth, this being particularly true when light intensity is low, which can often be the case early in the year. With an early tomato crop exceptional quantities of nitrogen can induce soft growth which renders plants very susceptible to disease attack. The lush green colouration and excessively curled foliage caused by an excess of nitrogen show quite clearly that the plant is much concerned with the process of photosynthesis carried on in the leaves.

Nitrogen is taken up by the plant as highly soluble nitrate, usually under 'conventional' soil-based cultural systems which have become converted by soil bacteria from ammonia to nitrite and then nitrate. Plants can also absorb liquid ammonia in limited quantities. Where tomatoes are grown in soil-less media it is necessary to provide a form of nitrogen which is immediately available, without recourse to the initial bacterial action.

The availability of nitrogen to the plant in soil-containing media will obviously be largely dependent on the rate of bacterial activity, and this will depend on soil temperature and also on whether the bacteria are inhibited or otherwise by organisms such as engulfing protozoa, by waterlogging, lack of air, consolidation or other factors. The flush of nitrogen which will invariably result following partial sterilisation of soil (see Chapter 12) is due to the ability of the thick-walled ammonifying bacteria to survive normal sterilisation temperatures in contrast to other types, including bacteria-engulfing protozoa, which are killed off. Pest and disease control is of course the main reason for sterilisation, the dissipation of plant toxins also being an important issue.

The constant breakdown of organic matter, which goes on continuously, does of course result in the formation of carbon dioxide (CO_2) which, with water, forms a weak acid solution in the soil, and it is this weak acid which is one of the main agents in dissolving not only nitrogen, but the other elements. The highly soluble nature of nitrogen makes it extremely vulnerable to leaching (washing out), which is one reason why watering should not be carried out to excess in glasshouse culture. Waterlogging will of course reduce bacterial activity which in turn results in a lack of nitrogen available to the plant.

Excess of nitrogen in tomato plants is usually shown quite clearly by lush unproductive growth, and shortage by pale, often yellow, small-leaved lank plants. Plants taking up too much ammonia show varied symptoms, blossom end rot or 'black bottoms' on fruit is thought to be one of these (see p171). Nitrogen and ammonia are very soluble, hence the possible need for flooding after heat sterilisation (see Chapter 12).

To summarise: nitrogen is needed in large amounts by tomatoes. An excess produces lush soft growth, which is disease-prone. Stems are usually also very thick. A shortage produces pale small leaves, often yellowed.

Phosphorus Phosphorus is associated with all life and is a basic constituent of every living cell, whether animal or plant. Plants generally require considerable amounts of phosphorus, and yet the tomato is not particularly demanding in this respect, especially in relation to the quantities of potassium and nitrogen needed. Natural supplies of phosphorus exist in many types of soil, but there can also be a deficiency of phosphorus, not necessarily because of actual shortage, but because what there is is in an unavailable form.

The net effects of phosphorus on the tomato plant are so all-embracing that it is difficult to single out its precise function. As phosphate is essential for the whole process of life, it is essential for all root growth, and tomatoes are no exception. Young plants benefit particularly from it, but the benefits persist right to maturity by hastening flower and fruit development.

Phosphorus is available to plants as phosphoric acid (P_2O_5) when it has been dissolved in the weak acid produced in the soil by various processes. This includes phosphorus contained in plant debris and made available initially

The Main Types of Bulky Organics used in Tomato Growing
(Most of these organic materials contain trace elements in addition to the main elements stated)

	Percentage in fresh samples			*Comments*
Average quality	Nitrogen (N)	Phosphorus (P_2O_5)	Potash (K_2O)	
Farmyard manure	0.43	0.19	0.44	Farmyard manure is found to vary considerably and for tomato culture should be well decomposed. Contains reasonably balanced quantities of the main nutrients.
Poultry manure	2.1	1.21	0.60	Note the high nitrogen content (richer than farmyard manure) which gives rise to problems when used too liberally for tomatoes.
Sewage sludge	2.31	1.29	0.25	Useful for tomatoes grown out of doors. Nitrogen content very variable.
Compost				Extremely variable quantities of nutrients. The important issue is the available balanced form of the nutrients. Well-made compost should contain the full range of plant nutrients in balanced quantities but be very careful to avoid any plant material contaminated by hormone weedkillers (eg grass verges).
Seaweed	0.4–0.8	0.1–0.2	1–2	A useful form of organic matter fairly rich in potash. Should be used fresh or composted.
Peat	0.7–3	0.1–0.2	0.1–0.3	Peat is used mainly to 'condition' soil for tomato cultivation, as top dressing or mulch, as main or sole ingredient of soil-less composts (*see* p 67). pH of sphagnum peat is 3.5–4.0. Peat nutrient content released very slowly. Wood bark also used, but less widely.

by the process of composting and thereafter by normal soil processes. The problem is that phosphorus is highly insoluble and, of the total present, only a very small proportion is actually available to plants. In acid soils much of the phosphate combines with iron and aluminium to form insoluble compounds, which shows the need to keep soils well supplied with calcium (lime), although liming is not the full answer as insoluble calcium phosphate can be formed.

It is thought that when phosphorus is added to a soil the actual phosphorus applied becomes insoluble but it releases a quantity of previously unavailable phosphorus for use. Observation of the phosphate found by analysis to be present in older tomato soils in considerable quantities shows quite clearly that tomato plants themselves are able to extract considerable amounts of phosphorus from the soil reserves – so much so that it may be unnecessary to apply any phosphorus at all for many years when cropping such soils.

Lack of phosphorus in the tomato plant is indicated by a bluish colouration, this symptom frequently being exhibited by chilled plants unable to assimilate the phosphorus they properly require. Symptoms of excess phosphorus are difficult to define, possibly because amounts surplus to plant requirements are either lost by drainage or alternatively become unavailable.

To summarise: phosphorus is only needed in limited amounts by tomatoes. A shortage leads to bluish discolouration and lateness of general development. An excess is difficult to detect visually.

Potassium (K) Like the other main elements, potassium is an essential constituent of all living matter, being required in very large amounts, especially by the tomato. Potassium is a constituent of many types of rock and is generally present naturally in larger quantities than nitrogen and phosphorus, yet only a small proportion may be available to the growing plant. It is taken up in solution as potassium oxide (K_2O), when it seems to be largely connected with carbohydrate formation and the rate at which photosynthesis occurs.

Potassium is very important for flowers and fruit, and therefore very necessary for tomatoes, which form a high proportion of fruit in relation to total plant bulk. Potassium improves quality and flavour and imparts a measure of disease resistance to plants, in this way contrasting with the effects of nitrogen. This means that a shortage of potassium invariably results in lush soft growth with an almost bluish hue and with marginal leaf necrosis. Research has shown that potassium has a great effect on the regulation of water uptake. Much of the success in tomato growing lies, in fact, in supplying the correct balance of nitrogen and potassium at the right time (*see* Chapter 4).

To summarise: Potassium is needed in large amounts by the tomato. A shortage leads to lush soft growth with marginal leaf necrosis, an excess to hard stunted growth and very dark green colouration.

Magnesium This is a highly important element for tomato plants, being closely tied up with chlorophyll formation, and when it is lacking or unavailable the photosynthetic process is affected, with the result that browny-orange areas appear on the older leaves between the veins, especially in the sunniest parts of the greenhouse where photosynthesis is at its highest. Magnesium also acts as a carrier for phosphate and regulates the uptake of other nutrients, including the translocation of carbohydrates around the plant. It can be seen, therefore, that magnesium has a major part to play in tomato culture, and for this reason it cannot generally be taken for granted that there is sufficient magnesium present in the soil. There is much to be said for organic growing systems where there is generally a more balanced approach to nutrition as, without doubt, excess quantities of potash can result in magnesium deficiency.

To summarise: magnesium is required in fairly large quantities by tomatoes. A shortage causes interveinal chlorosis (yellowing) of leaves which occurs on the lower leaves first and gradually travels up the plant. Orange areas usually develop later. The sunny side of the greenhouse is worst affected. Plants grown in a light type of soil where potash has to be used frequently suffer most from magnesium deficiency. The results of an excess are difficult to define, although surplus magnesium will generally affect the salt content of the soil or growing medium by affecting the process of osmosis. This effect can be used with care to control plant vigour.

Calcium Calcium is present naturally in various forms, particularly in phosphate-containing soils. Apart from neutralising the acid excretions of plants and stimulating bacterial action, calcium is a constituent of all plants, especially of the cell walls. Calcium has an important part to play in the base exchange mechanism which operates to supply plants with nutrients. It also serves to bring together the fine particles of clay to form crumbs, a process called flocculation. The amount of exchangeable calcium in the soil-growing media or in nutrient solutions is measured by what is called the pH scale, which ranges from 1 to 14, 7 being the neutral point between sourness (low pH figures) and sweetness (high pH figures).

For tomato growing in soil-containing media, the pH figure should be between 6 and 6.5, but for growing in soil-less media where there is less bacterial action, at least initially, lower pH figures seem to be quite acceptable. The amount of exchangeable calcium in the soil can greatly affect the availability of other elements, and vice versa, especially of ammonia and potassium, which can shut off or immobilise the calcium. Too low a pH figure can result in toxicity of manganese, too high a figure in unavailability of manganese.

To summarise: calcium is required in reasonable quantities for tomato plants. A shortage leads to general lack of vigour, usually with the yellowing symptoms typical of nitrogen shortage or with whitening at growing points. Blossom end rot is a typical symptom of calcium deficiency. The results of excess are difficult to define, although iron shortage is the main symptom of a high pH figure (*see below*).

Iron Iron is much concerned with the photosynthetic process and shortage of it usually turns leaves pale, and in severe cases white. Iron is relatively insoluble at normal pH figures, and becomes more so at high pH figures, when insoluble salts may be formed. Excess iron is supposedly toxic to plants, although I have personal experience of a considerable excess of iron being applied in error to tomato plants with no ill effects! But excess application is not to be generally recommended.

To summarise: iron is an element essential to tomatoes in small amounts.

A shortage leads to yellowing or whitening of the leaf. The results of excess are difficult to define accurately.

Manganese Again, this is much concerned with photosynthesis, and shortage of it causes chlorosis or mottling of the leaves. Manganese deficiency can often occur at high pH levels with young rapidly growing plants, and can disappear once the plants' growth rate decreases. Manganese toxicity is far more serious than deficiency, causing an intense blue-black colouration at growing points and a drooping down of leaves. It can occur in acid soils, or most commonly following steam sterilisation.

To summarise: manganese is an essential element in tomato culture, but small amounts only are required. A shortage leads to chlorosis and mottling of leaves, especially when the plant is young. An excess causes a blackish colouration of growing points, coupled with a drooping appearance.

Boron Although at one time boron was not thought to be an important element in tomato nutrition, it has attracted considerable attention in recent years and must now be considered as having a vital role to play in the general growth of plants, deficiency causing shrivelling and yellowing of growing points. In some cases a brown corky layer can form below the skin around the fruit. Usually sufficient quantities are available *in the soil* for all normal needs.

To summarise: boron is required in small amounts, but its presence is essential. A shortage causes shrivelling or yellowing of growing points, bushy side shoots and possibly corkiness under the skin of fruit. An excess is unlikely to occur, but would cause marginal shrivelling on leaves. (Boron is used as a weedkiller!)

Sulphur Sulphur has an important part to play in general plant nutrition, but it is difficult to be precise about its function. A general symptom of shortage is stems becoming thin and stiff. As sulphur is present in many fertilising materials, its shortage is seldom a problem.

The other elements referred to on page 48 are unlikely to give rise to any severe complications with tomato plants under normal cultural conditions (*see* 'Spectrochemical Analysis' on p60). Copper deficiency can arise in certain circumstances and is typified by very thin, woody stems, more so than with sulphur deficiency. It is easy to become supersensitive to deficiencies and excesses, and clearly the average grower or gardener must compromise and attend to the obvious irregularities. Specialist advice should always be obtained in a commercial situation. For NFT or rockwool systems see Appendix 3.

TOMATO BASE-FERTILISER FORMULATIONS

Proprietary base fertilisers are available in standard, high-potash and high-nitrogen forms. Details of composts and soil-less media are discussed in Chapter 4.

An *average* analysis is as follows, but can be variable:

Base fertiliser	Nitrogen %	Phosphorus %		Potash %
	N	P and P_2O_5 Sol	Insol	K_2O
'Standard'	9.5	9	0.5	13.2
High potash	6	10	0.5	17.5
High nitrogen (seldom necessary)	12	5.5	0.5	6
John Innes base (use as high potash)	5.2	7	0.5	10

The use of base fertiliser is discussed in Chapter 7, but generally speaking high-potash base is used following the sterilisation by heat of soil-containing media, or for vigorous varieties on unsterilised soils. Standard base is used when the growing medium is fresh or has been chemically sterilised. High-nitrogen base may be used for soils thought to be deficient in nitrogen. *When buying growbags containing prepared compost, base dressings are unnecessary.* If in any doubt about base fertiliser application, soil analysis is useful (*see* Chapter 4).

Some Fertilisers used in Tomato Culture					
Type	N %	P_2O_5 %	K_2O %	Other elements %	Comments and rates of use
Hoof and horn meal	12–14				An organic but expensive form of nitrogen much used in tomato base fertiliser and composts. Release of ammonia can be rapid but complete release of nitrogen content is over a period. Use up to 4oz per sq yd ($136g/m^2$).
Dried blood	11–12	1–2	1		Main use is in 'safe' top dressing for tomatoes at 1–2oz per sq yd (34–$68g/m^2$) as a quick source of nitrogen. Although organic, its release of nitrogen is rapid. Also useful diluted at up to 2oz per gal (12g/1 litre).
Nitro-chalk	25			Carbonate of lime	Inorganic quick-acting source of nitrogen. Main use is for tomatoes requiring an urgent 'kick'. Frequently used where 'virus check' occurs (*see* Chapter 11). Use at rates of ½–1oz per sq yd (17–34g/m^2). (Percentages subject to change.)

Some Fertilisers used in Tomato Culture (continued)

Type	N %	P₂O₅ %	K₂O %	Other elements %	Comments and rates of use
Nitrate of potash or potassium nitrate	12–15		46		Inorganic, convenient, quick source of nitrogen. Best used as a liquid fertiliser.
Ammonium nitrate	35				Inorganic. Used as a constituent of liquid fertilisers.
Urea	46				Organic. Used mainly as a constituent of liquid feed. It can be used 'dry' at 1oz per sq yd (34g/m²) as an organic source of nitrogen. The more sophisticated form is urea formaldehyde (Nitroform) 38% N, releasing the nitrogen over a period. Use as directed.
Ammonium phosphate (Mono and Di)	12–20	53–61			Inorganic. Used mainly in slow-release-type fertilisers, seldom as a separate entity.
Bonemeal	1–5	15–32			Organic. Not used greatly in tomato culture but would be useful in soil very low in phosphates, applied in addition to base feed. Use at 3–4oz per sq yd (101–135g/m²).
Super-phosphates of lime		17–19			Inorganic. Best form of phosphates for tomato culture, used generally as a constituent of base feeds and in composts. Can be used at up to 4oz per sq yd (135g/m²).
Sulphate of potash			48–50		Inorganic. Use at 1–2oz per sq yd (34–68g/m²) as quick source of potash. Can also be diluted in water at 1oz per gal (7g/1 litre).
Epsom salt \ Keiserite				Magnesium oxide 9 \ Magnesium oxide 16	Inorganic. Use up to 3–6oz per sq yd (101–203g/m²) for tomatoes. Used also as foliar feed at 2lb per 10gal (10g/litre) with a spreader.

Some Fertilisers used in Tomato Culture (continued)					
Type	N %	P_2O_5 %	K_2O %	Other elements %	Comments and rates of use
Lime (hydrated) (ground) (magnesian)				Calcium oxide 68 Calcium 47 Magnesium oxide 10–40 Calcium oxide 50–80	The main form of lime used for tomato culture is ground limestone, a relatively slow-acting form of calcium. Magnesian limestone is frequently used for tomato growing as it contains magnesium. Both forms are used according to soil analysis but generally at 8oz per sq yd (270g/ m²). For quantities used in soil-less media see Chapter 4.
Calcium nitrate	11				Useful source of nitrogen and calcium.
Fishmeal	6	7	3		(Percentages variable).
Rock phosphate		30	11		Available over a period.
Rock potash			10		Available over 2–3 years.

4

Soil, Nutrients and Growing Media

UNDERSTANDING SOIL AND TISSUE ANALYSIS

Soil analysis in its various forms comes in for much criticism by soil chemists, who consider that most systems of analysis do not truly reflect the quantities of nutrients actually available to the plants. Recent years have seen the introduction of different systems of reporting soil-analysis figures, and also the increased use of spectrochemical analysis of both soil and tissue, and the 'spot' analysis of plant tissue.

The full technical implications of soil analysis are not likely to be grasped by either gardener or grower, and it will suffice for practical purposes to describe the various analysis systems fairly broadly.

Soil Testing Kits

These take various forms and can establish: (1) the acidity or alkalinity of the soil by testing with litmus paper, (2) an approximate pH figure by means of a series of litmus-paper tests, and (3) a remarkably accurate pH figure by using indicator fluid, either separately or in combination with barium sulphate as a precipitant. Complete soil testing kits using indicator fluids are also available for pH figures and to show the relative availability or percentage deficiency of the three main elements – nitrogen, phosphorus and potash. While they cannot be considered nearly as accurate as laboratory analysis, soil testing kits have the virtue of giving quick 'on the spot' guidance, thus eliminating the unavoidable delays in laboratory analysis. Small pH and salt meters are now available and are useful.

Laboratory Analysis

This is undertaken in most parts of Britain, through official advisory bodies, societies or commercial firms. The range and method of analyses and the system of reporting vary, but the information which is normally available is set out in the following paragraphs. There will probably be a charge for analysis, although some commercial firms still provide free analysis for their customers.

Organic matter The level of organic matter is a very useful guide to the tomato grower and is reported either as a percentage figure or simply as 'low', 'medium' or 'high'. A figure of 8–12 per cent (including moisture) would be described as a 'good' organic matter content for a tomato soil. Trench systems of compost application ensure that levels of organic matter are optimal.

Lime requirement The lime requirement is of considerable interest to the tomato grower, and this is given in order to adjust to a pH figure, the norm being between pH 5.5 and pH 6.5 (note that lower pH figures are acceptable for soil-less media), lime being added generally in the form of ground limestone. As lime requirements are given per square area of soil to a depth of 9–10in (23–30cm), some conversion to bulk is desirable. Despite metrication the bushel (22 x 10 x 10 inches) (36 litres) will probably continue to be used for some time in horticulture, and there are approximately 5 bushels in a square yard (to 9in/23cm depth), 51–2 in a square metre, and 22 (21.7) in a cubic yard, 27 in a cubic metre (*see* p71–3).

A soft, fine-particled calcium carbonate or chalk is frequently used for growing tomatoes, and this has the same calcium value as ground limestone. Hydrated lime is 'hotter' than ground limestone and only three-quarters of the amount is required for the same liming value, but it is not generally advised as it can scorch foliage. There is a time lag between the application of the ground limestone and the attainment of the correct pH.

Available nitrogen (N) This is not a test carried out by every laboratory, because the nitrogen level varies greatly according to the rate of bacterial action as dictated by season, temperature, and whether soil has been heat sterilised or not. The nitrogen availability can be assessed in various ways, for example as ammonia or total nitrogen, in mg/litre (parts per million (ppm)).

Index figures are also being used by some bodies, and it is necessary to refer to tables for their significance in relation to other methods of reporting. The usual terms relating to availability – low, medium and high – are used in addition in most cases, yet correct interpretation of the results by an experienced chemist or horticulturalist is essential. Tomatoes require a 'high' nitrogen figure for optimum growth.

Available potassium (K_2O or K) Stated as mg/litre (or ppm) quoted as low, medium or high, this is a very useful guide to quantities of potash available in the soil. For tomatoes the figure should be 500–700 mg/litre (ppm) K (in soil, and stated as 'high' (*see also* 'Soluble salt content' below). Where index factors are quoted to standard scales the figure would be 4–5.

Available phosphorus (P or P_2O_5) The figures are reported as for potash, in respect of available phosphorus, although this is a difficult figure to reconcile with true availability to plants because of the 'fixing' of phosphorus in the soil. Old tomato borders which have been cropped over a number of years frequently show a very high level of phosphorus. Ideal figures are 41–70 mg/litre (ppm) P (in soil), or index 4–5 and stated as 'high'.

Magnesium Most laboratories will report magnesium levels, whether high, medium or low. Index factors of 3–5 are normal for tomatoes. A calcium/magnesium ratio of 10/1 is the aim.

Soluble salt content (pC or Cf – conductivity factor) This is a very important figure for the tomato grower, and one to which considerable attention
must be paid in view of the respective osmotic pressures in the cell sap and
the soil water (*see* p44); pC figures of 2.8–3.0, or Cf of 16–10 (index, around
3) are desirable for tomato growing, as salt concentrations exercise a means
of control on growth. The pC scale is now converted to microsiemens, eg
2800–3000 microsiemens. Higher concentrations of salt indicated by a lower
pC figure, in the order of 2.6 (Cf 25, index 5–6), are so dangerously near
osmotic equilibrium that growth of the tomato plants is very likely to be
adversely affected, except for cherry tomatoes which *must* be grown at high
salt concentrations. Roots may in fact be chemically damaged if the salt concentrations are too high. Spot checks carried out regularly are very useful for
commercial growers before and after planting, and many of them feel that the
purchase of a salt concentration meter is worth while. Growing media can be
checked after mixing; generally all proprietary media for full-season growing
are already at the correct pC level, or alternatively will reach the correct level
if accurately self-formulated.

Spectrochemical Analysis

This determines the levels of micro-elements such as zinc, manganese, copper
and iron. Both soils and plant tissue can be examined, but in each instance
spectrochemical analysis would only normally be carried out by advisory
bodies following abnormalities in growth.

Tissue Analysis

Here plant tissue is analysed either by spectrochemical or some other method to determine the actual nutrient level of the tissue, an extremely valuable
operation provided there can be comparison between healthy tissue and that
showing abnormal growth. There is an increasing use of tissue analysis for
quick checks on the nutrient level in the plant.

Other Methods of Analysis

It is claimed that the observation of the growth made by various fungal and
other cultures introduced under laboratory conditions to samples of soil gives
a much more realistic picture of the actual availability of nutrients than the
normal extraction method of soil analysis.

Methods of analysis based on the utilisation of 'labelled' radioactive elements
are also used in research work. By means of these it is possible to follow the
progress of elements through the plant tissue.

But the normal visual check on growth still remains a highly important
procedure in growing, and this is especially true in respect of the tomato
plant, which shows a quick reaction to excesses and shortages of main and
micro-nutrients.

Eelworm Determination

Soil or compost infested with the cysts of the female *Globodera rostochiensis* (potato cyst nematode or PCN) which contain visible larvae should preferably not be used for tomato culture. The crippling effect of potato cyst eelworm (PCN) on tomatoes is discussed in Chapter 11; it is obviously important to know whether or not a soil contains eelworm cysts. An eelworm count giving the number of eelworm per gram of soil and whether they contain live larvae, is usually available from advisory services.

Disease, Pest and Weed Potential of Soil

Detection by pathological means of the presence of tomato diseases before a soil is used for tomato growing is not a very satisfactory procedure, although it can be done in part by examining root debris of the previous crop. The best guidance is, however, the previous cropping history of the soil. Many pests can be visually detected, especially wireworm, and the same is true of the vegetative portions of bad perennial weeds.

The Importance of Representative Sampling

Soils sent for analysis should be entirely representative of the main bulk of the growing medium. Where border soils are concerned, several small samples should be taken with a trowel, auger, or other instrument which will conveniently lift a small quantity of soil from a depth of 5–6in (13–15cm). The total bulk of this sample should weigh about 2lb (1kg), and should be placed in a polythene bag and clearly labelled for dispatch to the advisory body. One 2lb (1kg) sample will generally be suitable for an area of up to 1,000sq ft (92m²), although there should be no hesitation in taking further samples of 'good' and 'bad' areas.

Growing media may be sampled throughout the mixture by lifting small portions with a trowel to bulk into a sample. Samples are best taken from the formulated growing medium, although there is a lot to be said for sampling doubtful ingredients before mixing. This applies especially to sand, loam, or very acid peat where a pH test may suffice. Always label samples clearly.

Fertiliser and Liquid Feed Analysis

The analysis of fertilisers is generally unnecessary, as the quality control is very strict at the manufacturing stage. Analysis can be useful in the case of doubtful identity. A frequent form of analysis in the case of soil-less systems is to check the salt concentration (pC or Cf) of liquid fertilisers when diluted and ready for crop application.

THE NUTRIENT REQUIREMENTS OF TOMATOES
Estimating Nutrient Needs

Estimating quantities of nutrients or using soil-analysis figures to cater for the actual nutrient needs of tomatoes either in borders or in formulated compost is not exactly a simple matter, nor can it even be known whether all the nutrients given are all available to the plant. A further complication is

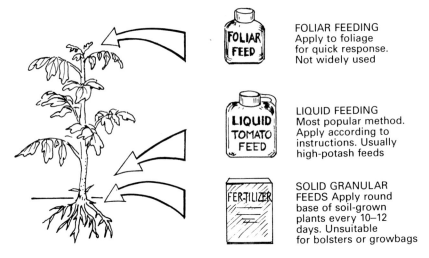

FOLIAR FEEDING
Apply to foliage
for quick response.
Not widely used

LIQUID FEEDING
Most popular method.
Apply according to
instructions. Usually
high-potash feeds

SOLID GRANULAR
FEEDS Apply round
base of soil-grown
plants every 10–12
days. Unsuitable
for bolsters or growbags

Fig 21 Different ways of feeding tomato plants in small-scale culture

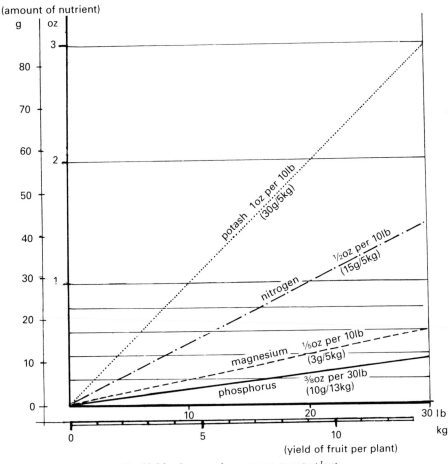

Fig 22 Nutrient requirements per tomato plant

that the differing performance of each plant makes its own special demands, which in simple terms means that a tomato plant yielding only 6lb (2.5kg) of fruit will require fewer nutrients than a plant yielding 20lb (9kg) of fruit. The stated requirements for the major nutrients for different cropping levels are subject to some variation, but fall broadly into the following levels:

Fruit Yields and Nutrient Needs					
50 tons per acre 10lb (4.5kg) per plant		100 tons per acre 20lb (9kg) per plant		150 tons per acre 30lb (14.5kg) per plant	
lb	kg	lb	kg	lb	kg
Potash	900	400	1,800	800	2,700	1,200
Nitrogen	500	225	1,000	450	1,500	675
Phosphorus	100	45	200	90	300	135
Magnesium	120	55	240	110	360	115
Calcium	600	270	1,200	540	1,800	810

Note These figures are approximate and relate mainly to the production of tomatoes under border-growing conditions, with their attendant drainage loss.

The graph (*see* Fig 22) shows quite clearly that potassium, nitrogen, magnesium and phosphorus are required in considerable quantities, each in amounts which are relatively consistent. The graph reduces these figures to the requirements for individual plants. Calcium is not included, as it is best supplied by adjustment of the pH figure; the need of soil for calcium varies considerably. Note that lower pH figures are acceptable with soil-less culture systems. For higher yields calculate proportionally.

Allowing for drainage loss in use of 15–20 per cent or more, and for the 'fixing' of phosphorus, it is safe to assume that about 50 per cent of the nutrient applied is available to the plants in nitrogen and potash and 20 per cent with phosphorus. If a soil when analysed is found to be low in all nutrients, one would therefore set out to apply about 50 per cent of the plants' total needs initially in the form of a base fertiliser, and supply the balance by seasonal feeding. This method does not necessarily apply to soil-less media or organic growing methods: it is generally the practice to have soil-less media lower in nutrient status early in the season, and to apply regular applications of liquid fertiliser. The reason for this is outlined later in this chapter.

While it is possible to work out the individual requirements of plants, it is not a procedure to be advised. One can by accurate analysis determine what nutrients are available to the plant and supplement these if, or as, required, and advice is generally given by the person or body reporting the analysis results. More generally, however, with border growing, a tomato base dressing is given at a fairly standard rate, basing the analysis of the dressing given on a number of factors (*see* p55). Around 8oz per sq yd (270g/m²) is a normal dressing. It should also be noted that the percentage nutrients present in fertilisers are quoted as K_2O and P_2O_5, lower figures of potassium (K) and phosphorus (P) actually being available. Roughly only about half the crop's needs are supplied by base dressings. Few soils are completely devoid of nu-trients, however, and generally speaking the picture is built up as follows:

	Requirements for plant
Base application 8oz	One-third is met
Plus reserve nutrients in soil	One-half is met
Plus top dressing in summer with solid ferti-lisers, ie 6 or 7 dressings of 1oz per sq yd (34g/m²) (roughly equal to total amount of base dressing) or more continuous liquid-fertiliser application	Requirements are fully met

These days there is of course widespread use of growbags or bolsters which contain compost with an adequate and correctly balanced quantity of plant nutrients, which means that base application is not required. Other systems of culture such as ring culture, straw bales, rockwool, perlite and nutrient film technique (NFT) are discussed later (*see* Chapter 6 and Appendix 3). The basic nutrient needs of tomatoes with all systems is nevertheless similar, with the notable exception that in systems such as rockwool or NFT dissolved liquid fertilisers only are involved, not base dressings, which means that the total quantity of nutrients must be applied throughout the growing season.

Calculating Quantities of Liquid Feed

Working out the quantities of nutrients required to supplement base feeds, or to supply plant needs totally, can become a very complicated affair. Specialised tomato growers will be following a strict feeding programme, checked regularly with instruments which will, in the more sophisticated units, monitor nutrient supplies by computer. The smaller grower will find it worth investing in a salt meter to check the concentration of not only liquid feeds actually applied but of the salt concentration of the growing media. Even the simplest form of salt meter will give excellent guidance. Generally speaking, smaller growers or keen gardeners will tend to feed by observation rather than follow any complicated pro-gramme. It is of course possible to work out what liquid nutrient you actually apply.

To pick a very simple example, assume 2oz (56g) of dried blood is mixed up with 1gal (4.5 litres) of water. Assuming that one gallon (4.5 litres) is given to each plant then each plant receives 12 per cent (the nitrogen percentage of dried blood) of 2oz (56g) = ¹/₄oz (7g). If this quantity were given to several plants, which is much more likely, then the weight given to each plant would be proportional. When 'balanced' liquid fertilisers are applied, things become more complicated, it being important to remember that only a percentage of the nutrients contained in each has been given to the plants, not the total quantity of fertiliser (*see* table on p55–7).

Where liquid feeds are bought in instead of self-formulated, their analysis should be carefully checked. For simple and rough calculation purposes, if there is one gallon of liquid fertiliser which weighs about $11\frac{1}{2}$lb and the analysis is 10% N, 10% P_2O_5, and 10% K_2O, then very approximately 1lb of each nutrient will be applied when the whole gallon of liquid fertiliser is used. In metric terms the weight of nutrient applied for 1 litre of liquid fertiliser will be approximately one-tenth of the weight of 1 litre which is $11.5 \div 4.5 = 2.5$lb (1,120g). One-tenth of this is 112g.

As volume of liquid fertiliser and not weight is applied (although some fertilisers are sold by weight for dilution), it is necessary to make further calculations. Assuming $\frac{1}{10}$ gal of concentrated feed to 200 parts (by volume) of water and that the whole of this is applied, which is 200 parts (25 gal), then the plants would have received – in weight – $\frac{1}{10}$lb of each nutrient, and to calculate the quantities of fertiliser given to each plant it would be necessary to divide by the number of plants.

Thinking again in metric terms, simply take one-tenth of the total weight of liquid feed involved (or solid food dissolved) to arrive at the total quantities. This is better understood by referring to the table on p62 which gives both imperial and metric figures. *Obviously gardeners will be working in much smaller quantities of liquid fertiliser, but the procedure is similar, and I would strongly advise that they should think in terms of the total quantity of liquid fertiliser given over a period rather than make calculations on individual plant applications.*

The most important issues are: (1) the dilution rate, (2) the salt concentration of this dilution (preferably a pC of 2.8–2.9), (3) the balance of nutrients to each other – nitrogen to potash ratio, and (4) the total quantity of fertiliser given. More will be said about this in Chapter 10.

Important note It should be pointed out that fertiliser percentages are still quoted on P_2O_5 (for phosphorus) and K_2O (for potash) and that the actual quantities of phosphorus (P) and potash (K) available to the plants will be less than the P_2O_5 and K_2O figures stated. This makes accurate working out of the quantities of nutrients supplied still more difficult.

THE BASIC INGREDIENTS OF GROWING MEDIA
OR COMPOSTS

The following information is intended for gardeners wishing to mix their own growing media or composts rather than buying them in.

Loam

Loam is classified largely on the basis of the texture of the mineral particles, and taking particle size as:

sand 2.0–0.02mm   silt 0.02-0.002mm   clay   less than 0.002mm
The ideal composition would be in the order of 27 per cent clay, 28 per cent silt and less than 45 per cent sand. Apart from the mineral particle content, the organic matter content of loam is highly important by virtue of its colloidal properties, colloids having great virtue for the promotion of chemical change. The breakdown of the organic matter by micro-organisms results in the formation of humic gums which bind the finer particles together to form the ideal crumb structure, which in effect is a honeycombed collection of soil particles, allowing free passage of air and water. Loam derived from pasture turf, stacked and matured and then put through a shredder, serves as ideal organic matter and has an excellent built-in structure, especially if there has been a great deal of stock feeding on the pasture over the years. Lawns lifted and stacked are also frequently used as a source of loam.

On analysis loams show remarkable variation, ranging from 6 to 20 per cent organic matter (including moisture), a pH of around 5.5–6.5 (it could be lower or higher) and phosphate and potash levels of low to medium, according to the precise management of the turf. Obviously there is no such thing as a 'standard' loam, and indeed it would be difficult to give precise specifications for loam, as quality varies greatly according to source.

Supplies of good loam, free from pests, diseases and weeds, are therefore limited, especially in large consistent quantities for commercial and amateur use. Gardeners can often assess the quality of loam by feel. When squeezing in the hand, if it is possible to compress it so that it retains shape without stickiness, this indicates a clay soil. At the other end of the scale a sandy soil, particularly one devoid of organic matter, will quickly crumble following hand compression. There is not however the same emphasis placed on loam for tomato culture now as was the case years ago, and this, in many ways, is to be regretted.

The ideal water–air–nutrient balance of a really good loam is something which all plants appreciate, and the tomato is no exception, whether for propagation or for full-season growing. Yet recent experience with all peat or peat/sand composts such as rockwool or perlite seems to raise doubts about the real value of loam, particularly when the cropping performance of plants grown entirely in these other media is seen to be invariably of such a high order. The virtues of peat are discussed in the next section, but we may note at this point that the inconsistency of loam (as compared with peat) is its greatest weakness as a growing medium.

Loam, used as an ingredient of either seed, potting or growing media, should preferably be sterilised by heat, although chemical sterilisation is also reasonably effective (*see* Chapter 12).

The specification for medium loam is as follows:

7–27% clay   6–20% organic matter –
28–50% silt   generally around 10–12%
less than 52% sand

Peat

Peat is derived from deposits of organic matter which have been prevented from complete decay by the presence of excess moisture and/or acidity. 'Blanket bogs' develop in areas of fairly high elevation where rainfall is high, while 'basin bogs' are developed where moisture is trapped, thereby raising the water table. There are several ways of categorising peat, such as the nature of the plants composing it, the age and depth of the deposit, and whether deposits are pure or contaminated with river or rainwashed soils and silt. Age of deposit and depth of harvesting in relation to age are particularly important as far as horticultural peat is concerned. The degree of decomposition is very important, as this dictates the ability of the peat to remain cellular and thus serve as a porous breathing entity which will encourage vigorous root development, as opposed to merely being a mass of almost humic soggy organic matter which excludes air.

Brown cellular peats feel springy and dry, whereas black humic peats feel soggy and wet. Peats which are too new will still have the remains of plants running through them, and this is not particularly desirable for formulating growing media, nor, at the other end of the scale, is black humic peat by itself desirable, although a proportion of humic peat to provide trace-element supply is now favoured.

One way of classifying peat is by the Van Post scale, which is quite simply based on the colour of the water which can be squeezed out of the peat under a certain pressure. Peat is intrinsically acid in nature, especially if derived largely from sphagnum moss, and pH figures of 3.5–4.3 are usual. In contrast, sedge peats often have a pH of around 6.5 but are not so commonly used in horticulture, as supplies are somewhat limited compared to sphagnum peat, which is available in vast quantities in Britain and in Europe.

It is often puzzling to see the variety of grades of peat which are offered for sale, but a little thought makes it quite clear how they should be used: the coarse fibre-containing peats are for soil improvement and top dressing, whereas the fine granular-textured peats are much sought-after for growing media because of their excellent and consistent physical qualities. An average analysis of sphagnum peat is:

pH	N %	P_2O_5 %	K_2O %
3.5–4.3	0.7–3.0	0.1–0.2	0.1–0.3

Specification for peat It should be brown, of granular texture, having a springy feel, with cell walls which are intact so that a porous, breathing, growing medium is provided, capable of storing moisture and nutrients for gradual release to plants.

Sand

Sand largely tends to be graded according to particle size and, while for many building purposes this may be the important issue, for horticulture other criteria must be considered, and of these inertness is probably the most important. Ideally sand should have a pH of around 6.5 and be thoroughly washed, or alternatively naturally 'clean'. Too much calcium, iron or other mineral ingredients can severely upset the balance of a growing medium especially if sand is used in bulk.

Size gradings are usually stated quite clearly by the quarry concerned; generally speaking a mixture of fine and coarse sand is more useful for seed sowing and conventional propagation in pots, and for full-season growing media coarser sands are desirable, largely on the grounds of their physical separation and aerating effects. For growing-room activities where capillary watering systems are employed, a coarse sand is certainly advisable to ensure that the compost does not become soggy. The John Innes compost specifies a sand of $1/8$in (3–4mm) grist, which is very coarse, and here again aeration and drainage are the main considerations.

It is difficult to be dogmatic, not only on the gradings but even on the necessity of sand in growing media, as excellent results can be obtained by the use of 100 per cent peat composts. Obviously, therefore, there is considerable room for trial and error, although there are certain broad rules which should be followed.

Specification for sand It should be coarse, even-particled, chemically inert and clean, with a pH of 6.5–7.

Other Constituents of Growing Media

Apart from loam, peat and sand, other materials are now being used for the formulation of growing media, and these include the following:

Vermiculite An expanded mica, this is an absorbent, light, relatively inert material with a large surface area. Vermiculite is largely used in soil-less mixes, which are based on variable percentages of vermiculite to peat – generally around 75 per cent peat to 25 per cent vermiculite (by bulk), or even a lower proportion of vermiculite.

Perlite This is a volcanic ash, and again is relatively inert. Remarkably light, it separates components physically, simply because of its large bulk. While it can be used as an additive to peat or soil/sand mixes, it has in recent years been used in pure form (as discussed later).

Expanded polystyrene and other synthetics Used in rather similar proportions to vermiculite and perlite, these materials are usually waste from plastics factories and are now being used for compost formulation. While chemically inert, they usually remain a separate entity within the soil, and indeed can remain undecomposed in the soil for an indefinite time.

Basically synthetics come in three forms – polystyrene foam, polyurethane foam and urea formaldehyde. The first two, while standard enough in specification, suffer the disadvantage of being too cellular in nature, which means quite simply that they are unable to act as a colloidal material in the same way as decomposing peat or rotting turf. Urea formaldehyde is, however, a different material, being cottonwool-like and absorbent, and in essence resembling a synthetic peat.

Polystyrene and polyurethane foam, while physically valuable in soils or composts by virtue of their mechanical soil-conditioning powers, have their limitations and are virtually incapable of storing moisture and encouraging chemical change. Synthetics have high insulation properties and therefore impart warmth to a growing medium – and they are of course very light to handle. Experimental work in Germany, America and Britain has shown quite clearly that remarkably good results have been obtained where urea formaldehyde foams are used, not only in growing media, but also for outside crops. Roots have shown excellent development in the area of dispersal of the foam, proving that it gives excellent aeration and growth opportunities. Much research work, however, remains to be done before these materials are commercially marketable in quantity, yet I feel that it will not be long before they are generally used in other spheres of horticulture, and that the small plastic blocks now available will be superseded.

Waste paper and other materials Experimental work has been carried out with waste paper and a number of other materials as growing media. Pulverised wood bark has been used with some success for tomato culture in troughs or other containers. Provided it has been effectively composted, nitrogen deficiency should not be a problem but one cannot say that wood bark is an ideal medium for tomato culture.

5 Mineral rockwool systems of tomato culture have, in the late eighties, become widespread. Note the method of placing the 'pots' on top of the slabs. The grain of the mineral rockwool can either be horizontal or vertical

Rockwool Mineral rockwool in slab form has made a very considerable impact on the commercial tomato growing industry but so far there has been little penetration into the amateur market. The reason for this is that rockwool culture is a form of hydroponics and does involve considerable accuracy with nutrient supplies. The broad principles of rockwool culture are discussed later *but it is stressed that it is a matter better taken up with the specialist suppliers of such systems.* Rockwool granules are now available as a compost additive.

Basic Principles of Soil-less Culture

(*See also* Appendix 3 on Nutrient Film Technique.)

The variable nature of loam, difficulties of supply and of transport, the possible presence of pests, diseases and weeds, and the problem of sterilisation, are undoubtedly troubles of sufficient magnitude to detract from its popularity as a growing medium. It was to be expected that alternatives to loam would be sought on a wide horticultural front, and pioneer work in this direction was carried out at the University of California. The range of soil-less mixes suggested by this body has formed the basis for most of the research work into soil-less media which has been carried out in Europe, although research has been carried out independently in several countries for many years.

The characteristics of loam have been alluded to previously and, if we understand that loam has a mineral content, organic matter and a vast spectrum of micro-organisms, it can readily be appreciated that to use loam either by itself as soil comprising a greenhouse border, or as a constituent of compost, is to provide a nutrient-producing 'factory'. This applies not only to the nutrients already present in the loam, but to the loam as a vehicle for the chemical changes necessary before many nutrients can be made available to the plants. Loam has the capacity for storing up these nutrients, well in excess of the plant's needs, until required. Ideally, therefore, given a 'perfect' loam, cultural conditions are excellent.

By the same token, organic growers using copious supplies of compost incorporated into soils do provide excellent growing conditions for their plants.

As a complete alternative, plants can be grown in gravel, sand, perlite, rockwool or other inert media, or for that matter in water, provided that the nutrient requirements of the plant are met by the supply of soluble and palatable nutrients and there is sufficient aeration. Hydroponics is based upon this conception, and hydroponics is of course perfectly practical under a strictly controlled system of cultivation. Consider cellular peat with all its assets as a water-holding medium, coupled with inert sand to assist with aeration and drainage, and one appreciates the philosophy of soil-less culture. Peat is relatively sterile and so is sand, therefore some nutrients must be supplied in immediately available form, when they are then instantly available to the plants. It should be borne in mind, however, that micro-organisms soon invade the initially sterile medium from the plants in it, and from the atmosphere, thus producing cultural conditions approaching those offered by loam. The time for the breakdown of the peat will of course vary, and perhaps matters should not be unduly complicated by assuming that anything like the conditions of loam culture will occur in the short-term period of cultivation of the normal tomato crop.

More will be said later about soil conditioning for border soils of poor texture, to bring them up to the cultural standard necessary for tomatoes, but it should be remembered that a good loam-less or soil-less medium has an ideal texture from the outset, and this has proved to be highly advantageous. All is not on the credit side, however, as problems certainly exist with loam-less culture, not least of which is the apparent inability to 'soften' or 'buffer' nutrient availability to the plant, something which has both advantages and disadvantages according to the degree of precision exercised.

Composts and Growing Media
Soil-based Composts

John Innes Seed Compost
2 parts (by bulk) of loam (sterilised by heat preferably)
1 part by bulk of peat
1 part by bulk of coarse sand
To each bushel (22 x 10 x 10in) (36 litres) add $3/_4$oz (21g) ground limestone (1lb per cu yd or 600g/m³) and $1^1/_2$oz (42g) superphosphates (30oz per cu yd or 1,200g/m³).

John Innes Potting Compost
7 parts by bulk of loam
3 parts by bulk of peat
2 parts by bulk of coarse sand.

For No 1 compost, per bushel, add $3/_4$oz (21g) ground limestone (1lb per cu yd or 600g/m³) and $1/_4$lb (114g) of John Innes Base Fertiliser ($5^1/_4$lb per cu yd or 3.2kg/m³) (2 parts by weight hoof and horn meal, 2 parts superphosphates of lime and 1 part sulphate of potash).

For No 2 compost add $1^1/_2$oz (42g) ground limestone (2lb per cu yd or 1,200g/m³) and $1/_2$lb (226g) base fertiliser (10.5lb per cu yd or 6.4kg/m³).

For No 3 compost, add $2^1/_4$oz (63g) of ground limestone (3lb per cu yd or 1,800g/m³ and $3/_4$lb (340g) base fertiliser (16lb per cu yd or 9.5kg/m³).

Compost Mixing

Important note regarding metrication in compost mixing Changing over from imperial to metric measurements confuses many gardeners, in particular when it comes to measuring bulk quantities, especially when peat or peat-based composts are now invariably sold by bulk in litres. The popular measuring volume with gardeners generally is still the bushel, which is a box measuring 22 x 10 x 10in. A bushel has a volume of 8gal or, in other words,

Soil-less Composts 'Standard' Formulae			
Seed Sowing			
50% peat (by volume) 50% sand			
	per bushel (36 litres)	*per cu yd*	*per m³*
Superphosphates (18%)	1–2oz (28–56g)	1¼–2½lb (0.6–1.1kg)	800g–1.6kg
Potassium nitrate	½oz (28–56g)	10oz (280g)	400g
Ground limestone	4–6oz (114–170g)	5–7½lb (2.2–3.4kg)	3.2kg
Sulphate of potash	¼oz (8g)	5oz (141g)	200g
Or proprietary bases, such as Chempak, Vitax Q4 or Osmocote, at recommended rates.			
Pricking out and potting			
75% peat 25% sand			
	per bushel (36 litres)	*per cu yd*	*per m³*
Urea formaldehyde – winter	¾oz (21g)	1lb (454kg)	500g
(Nitroform) – spring	1oz (28g)	1¼lb (567g)	900g
– summer	1½oz (36g)	2lb (907g)	1,000g
Superphosphates (18%)	2oz (56g)	2½lb (3.41kg)	1,600g
Potassium nitrate	1oz (28g)	1¼lb (567g)	800g
Sulphate of potash	½oz (16g)	1¼lb (567g)	800g
Dolomitic limestone Ground limestone	3oz (85g) of each	4lb (1.8kg) of each	2.4kg of each
(Frit WN255 or 253A)	½oz (14g)	10oz (280g)	400g
Or proprietary bases, such as Chempak, Vitax Q4 or Osmocote, at recommended rates.			
Note Several firms now have bases with lime included in them.			

4 x 2gal buckets = 36 litres, and a bucket is probably the easiest measure for gardeners. For those considering larger bulks, there are nearly 22 bushels in a cubic yard and 27 bushels in a cubic metre, but it should be pointed out that these volumes are not likely to concern the average small gardener, though they will certainly be of concern to the commercial grower. If you want to work in smaller quantities, in metric terms, scale down the quantities to an appropriate level. For example, one 2 gallon bucket = 9 litres, or possibly now manufactured as 10 litres; so in broad terms divide all the bushel quantities by four and the weight of chemicals by four also. The alternative is to buy in compost as required, a procedure which has considerable merit although many with raw materials to hand do find it a lot cheaper to mix their own, using ready-mixed bases such as Chempak, Vitax Q4 or others, according to directions.

The ingredients for formulating compost should preferably be under cover and reasonably dry, although the peat should be moist. Mixing should be carried out on a solid, clean floor (making particularly certain that it is not contaminated with weedkiller or other noxious chemicals). Measure out the respective quantities in bulk (not necessary where peat is purchased with bulk stated), putting the largest quantity down first, then add the fertiliser accurately, turn once, then add the lime and turn twice more. Mixing the fertiliser with a small quantity of dry sand facilitates even distribution. *As*

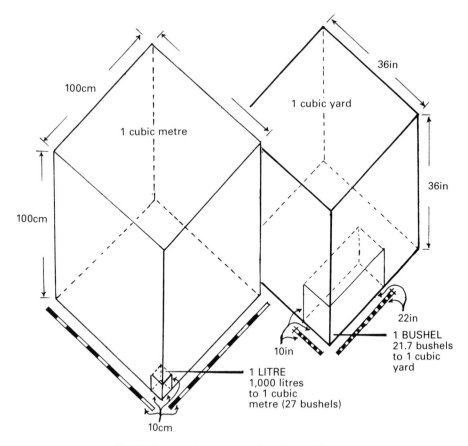

100cm

100cm

1 cubic metre

10cm

1 cubic yard

36in

36in

22in

10in

1 LITRE
1,000 litres
to 1 cubic
metre (27 bushels)

1 BUSHEL
21.7 bushels
to 1 cubic
yard

Fig 23 Comparative measures for volumes of compost

shrinkage occurs in mixing, ideally the fertiliser should be applied to the final measured bulk, but this can be difficult and laborious, and it is usual to allow for a 15–20 per cent shrinkage.

After mixing, a suitable period must be allowed, especially with soil-less media, for neutralisation to occur, ten days being the minimum period.

The keeping qualities of formulated composts vary. Those that contain slow-release forms of nutrients are more stable than those with 'straight' chemicals, although this is not always the case. With tomato border culture the importance of compost is at the propagation stage, at seed sowing and growing on, and the plants are then put into the borders which must be brought up to acceptable standards. Systems which involve compost for the full growing period are ring culture (in its various forms) and of course bolsters or growbags, where the compost is already formulated by the supplier. The newer systems of culture such as rockwool, perlite bags and of course NFT (nutrient film technique) will also involve compost, but at the propagation stage only. In some instances, as for rockwool culture, rockwool cubes are used. In the late 1980s it seems likely that growbags or bolsters will remain very popular with smaller-scale growers or amateur gardeners, while the larger growers will move still more positively into systems of culture without compost.

5
Propagation

Tomato propagation is a precise task, especially for the early crop, and is best attempted in a well-sited and well-designed greenhouse with adequate heating, preferably automatically controlled. The greenhouse itself should be clean and hygienic, having been carefully washed down during the winter with a good detergent, and the glass cleaned outside immediately prior to use so that maximum light can be transmitted. It is not generally realised how much light is excluded by dirty glass. Proprietary materials can be used for glass cleaning, or alternatively oxalic acid crystals, 1lb to 1 gallon of water (100g/litre), can be sprayed on and then washed off with a hosepipe, preferably when the greenhouse is empty.

Tomatoes can be propagated vegetatively from 4–5in (10–12$^1/_2$cm) cuttings rooted in a mixture of peat and sand at 56°F (18°C). A supply of cuttings must be available in the first case, which means the overwintering of parent plants if new young plants are to be produced early enough. Cuttings are useful for later crops, especially to make up shortages, but because of the prevalence of virus disease which would be transmitted by vegetative propagation, seed is therefore the safest and most reliable way of producing tomato plants.

Tissue culture (micro-propagation) is being used to propagate selected, disease-free, high-yielding plants for very early crops, but this must be done by specialised firms concentrating on tissue culture techniques. Unless good propagation facilities exist, it is often better to buy in plants when required from a nursery or garden centre, remembering that if quantities are large the plants should be ordered well in advance. For later crops, even for the gardener without a heated greenhouse, it is relatively easy to grow plants from seed and bring on plants at light windows or in heated porches or conservatories. Ideally a heated greenhouse is best, with its more even light distribution, but it must also be borne in mind that a lot can be done now with artificial light (*see* p38).

GERMINATION

Examination of a tomato seed shows that it has a relatively hard coat or testa which effectively protects the embryo from outside influences. Before germination can take place, this seed coat must be softened sufficiently to allow entry of water to trigger off the complicated process of germination. Much seed tends to lapse into what is called a dormancy period, and tomato seeds are no exception, although they are not so temperamental in this direction as many others. It is important that the temperatures should be of a sufficiently high level to induce germination, and this varies for the species of plant in question; there must also be a supply of air to allow respiration to take place.

Germination occurs by the production of, first, the radicle from which the root develops and then the plumule which goes up in the air, developing into the shoot. The first two seed leaves develop from the two cotyledons and the testa or coat of the seed should stay below compost level, but is frequently taken up with the seed leaves before falling off, and this increases the risk of virus infection, as the seed leaves may make contact with the outside of seed coats. Virus infection can also be transmitted to other plants by handling, but washing hands (or tools) in a 2 per cent solution of tri-sodium ortho-phosphate, barrier cream or household disinfectant is an excellent inhibitor.

Once leaves form, photosynthesis takes place and growth proceeds rapidly. What can be seen purely as a shoot and some leaves does not reveal what is going on inside the little plant. What in fact is happening is that flower trusses are being formed at a very early stage, and the result of considerable research has shown quite clearly that the temperature and light levels during this early formative period are critical in respect of the number of flowers, their time of appearance and, perhaps more importantly, the ability of these flowers to produce fertile pollen.

PROGRAMMING THE CROP

It is essential to decide exactly when seed is to be sown so as to produce plants which will be at the ideal stage at the right time for planting out. There must be co-ordination between temperature and light levels in the greenhouse, the latter varying regionally. The programmes quoted are therefore subject to modification, but are generally applicable to Britain and countries in similar latitudes.

Early Crop – No Supplementary Lighting

Seed sowing: mid-to end November (or earlier)
Potting up: end November to early December (8–12 days after sowing)
Spacing: 3 times: preferably in early mid-December (6–8in or 15–20cm), early to mid-January (12in or 30cm) and late January (15–16in or 38–40cm) if space allows
Planting: 1st to 3rd week February, or earlier (according to natural light levels)
Picking first fruit: mid-March to early April. (Fruit can be picked as early as mid February from October sowings.)
Note that with natural illumination it takes 12–14 weeks on average during the winter period from seed sowing to planting, and a further

6–7 weeks until first fruit is ripe. Note also that with later crops this time is considerably reduced. There is bound to be a considerable variation according to the area and the level of natural illumination. The better the light the shorter the propagating period. The earliest crops in Britain are normally produced in the south, and gradually become later as one journeys north. *It is essential to remember that very early crops should be attempted in good light areas and where cultural facilities are excellent.*

Early Crop – Supplementary Lighting

Seed sowing: late November to early December
Potting up: early November to late December (after 8–12 days); light treatment then given for 17–21 days or longer, according to rate of growth or until plants require considerable spacing
Spacing: this is carried out as for the unlit crop – generally 2–3 times
Planting: again variable, but generally from late January until early February, the earlier planting being achieved because of benefits derived from supplementary lighting
Picking first fruits: varies from mid-March until mid-April; the net effect of supplementary lighting will greatly depend on the precise area and type of season.
Note that on average it takes 9–10 weeks from seed sowing to planting with supplementary lighting. The same proviso about avoiding the early crop unless facilities are excellent and the area is well served with good natural light still applies. Indeed, plants raised under supplementary light systems can often be available far too early, unless supplementary light is used in the cropping houses.

Early Crop – Growing-room Propagation

Seed sowing: mid-December
Potting up: late December (after 8–12 days), when light treatment is given in the growing room for 14–21 days (12–16 hours daily) until first truss is initiated; small pots are used during light treatment, the plants being potted into $4^1/_4$in (11cm) pots afterwards
Spacing: into propagation house at 6 x 6in (15 x 15cm) or thereabouts, when some supplementary lighting is then valuable for 12–16 hours daily, for 7–10 days; space thereafter as necessary
Planting: from late January till early February (or earlier)
Picking first fruit: early March to early April (once again it must be stressed that the natural light level in any area is a vital factor in ripening bottom trusses of fruit).
Note that from seed sowing to planting can take as little as 7–8 weeks under ideal conditions, which is a saving of 4–5 weeks on natural propagation.

Second Early Crop – Natural Propagation

Seed sowing: early to mid-December
Potting up: late December to early January (after 8–12 days)
Spacing: as for early crops
Planting: end February to mid-March
Picking first fruit: late April to early May.

Note that propagating time varies greatly according to natural light level in the district but is generally 10–12 weeks. If lights are used, shortening of propagation period is likely.

Mid-season Crop

Seed sowing: late December to early January
Potting up: mid-January (8–12 days later)
Spacing: as before
Planting: mid-March to early April
Picking first fruit: early to mid-May.

Note that once again propagating time varies greatly according to the natural light level of the area, but is generally 9–10 weeks.

Late Crop

This applies to crops grown in moderately heated greenhouses.
Seed sowing: from mid-February
Potting up: late February
Spacing: generally on two occasions
Planting: mid- to late April
Picking first fruit: June.

Note that the propagating period from sowing to planting is now shortened to 6–8 weeks.

Later or Cold Crops

This includes the crop to follow on after an early crop and involves propagating with heat, but cold cropping in greenhouses (though in the north, mild heat in the greenhouse is always advantageous, especially at night to avoid high humidity).
Seed sowing: early to mid-March (in heat) until May for very late crops (double cropping)
Potting up: late March to early April (in heat for early period) until May for very late crops when potting can be into large pots
Spacing: as for late crop
Planting: early May to June (if standing outdoors until 'planting' time)
Picking first fruit: July to September.

Note that the propagation period has now shortened to around 5–7 weeks, perhaps 8 in colder areas.

6–10 Seed sowing. Fill the seed tray and strike it off level. Sow the seed evenly and cover lightly with compost. Good, even gemination is important

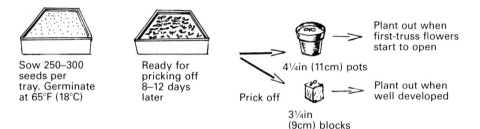

Sow 250–300 seeds per tray. Germinate at 65°F (18°C)

Ready for pricking off 8–12 days later

Prick off

4¼in (11cm) pots

Plant out when first-truss flowers start to open

3¼in (9cm) blocks

Plant out when well developed

Fig 24 Tomato propagation – from sowing to planting

SOWING AND POTTING
Sowing Procedure

Approximately 1,000 plants will be produced from ¼oz (5g) of seed. When sowing on a large scale use clean seed trays of plastic, polystyrene, or wood, each measuring approximately 14 x 9 x 2in (355 x 228 x 50mm). On a small scale, clean pots or seed pans should be used. A seed tray will take 250–3500 seeds and a 6in (15cm) pot about 60 seeds. Seed can also be sown individually in pots or cell trays, which avoids pricking off.

John Innes seed mix, all-peat, or peat/sand mixes (*see* Chapter 4) are suitably warmed, put into the receptacles, struck off level and then pressed down to within ¼in (½cm) of the top. A rich compost is not desirable for seed sowing, and for sowing direct into a pot it is safer to use liquid feeding once the young plants start showing rapid growth, than to use a rich potting compost. One major problem with seed sowing is the risk that ammonia damage will cause damping off, and this can occur when heat-sterilised John Innes compost has been used. It is less of a problem in soil-less mixes.

The seed is sown thinly (about 250–300 per standard seed tray) either broadcast or in shallow drills made with a piece of cardboard. It is then covered lightly by riddling on some compost or by closing the drills, then pressed in fairly firmly, with the object of keeping the seed testa below the compost level to avoid virus infection.

Alternatively seed can be spaced out at around 48 per box or thereabouts, or directly into small pots, procedures which avoid checks during pricking off; there is (according to various research findings) some virtue in this and it is easier if pelleted seed is used. Note that with rockwool systems seed can be sown direct in rockwool cubes. In my view it is better to sow in compost and prick off into the cubes.

Sowing Preparatory to Grafting

It is useful to have plants at a wider spacing preparatory to grafting, and spaced sowing at 24 seeds per tray is frequently practised, although the seed can be sown closer and pricked out into boxes at 24 per seed tray thereafter. One variety and one rootstock seed can be sown in individual pots. Note that it is generally advisable to sow the seed of the rootstock some 4–6 days before the variety owing to its slower germination.

Germination Techniques

Tomato seeds are 'light-hard', which means that they germinate better in darkness. After sowing seed, lightly water with a fine rose, taking care not to wash off the covering. Immersion of the base of smaller receptacles can be a useful technique, using water that is 'greenhouse warm'. If the receptacles are either stacked (in the case of seed trays) or covered with a sheet of paper or black polythene, moisture is conserved on the surface, assisting germination. I have found in recent years that an ideal method of ensuring good germination is to put seed trays into polythene bags in a warm spot when one can achieve nearly 100 per cent germination. Much use is made commercially of germinating cabinets, which are highly insulated shelved 'cupboards' where humidity is high and temperatures can be accurately controlled. As soon as germination occurs reasonably uniformly through the seeds (there will always be a proportion which do not germinate as quickly as the others) the boxes are unshaded, the covering or bags removed, and the seedlings given full light. Drying out must never occur during the actual germination period and additional watering may be necessary. Shading from hot sun may also be necessary.

Despite considerable controversy about germination temperatures for tomatoes, it has been generally agreed by plant physiologists that a 65°F (18°C) day and night temperature is generally acceptable. Higher temperatures will induce a higher percentage of rogues (short-jointed, squat, spiky-leaved plants with an even, true-leaf development, but which will remain unproductive). The production of rogues, although influenced by environmental conditions, is thought to be genetic. Gardeners who fear that they may have missed rogues during pricking off will have little difficulty in noting their squat, short-jointed, side-shooting habit at a later stage. Although they may look healthy and vigorous, they should not be planted as they will be totally unproductive, apart from producing a few chat fruits.

Containers for Potting

Within 8–12 days of sowing there should be a sufficiently high number of seedlings for potting. There are some differences of opinion concerning the virtues of early pricking off, especially as some authorities now believe that the first trusses are laid down at an earlier stage than was thought to be the case and that early pricking off could coincide with this critical period. In the absence of fully confirmatory evidence, however, the normal process of early pricking off is advised.

Research has shown quite clearly the virtue of pots that are large enough to contain the plants for a longer period, this particularly being the case with the earliest raised plants which are not planted until flowers are showing. A pot size of 4¼in (10–11cm) is generally recommended, and pots may be either of plastic, treated paper, polythene, peat or clay. Lattice pots

11 Square plastic pots are widely used for conventional plant raising

with slots at their bases are now very popular, particularly for NFT systems. Soil or peat blocks may also be used, provided that these are large enough to sustain growth, which generally means a large block size of approximately 3¹/₄in (8–9cm). Soil-less materials are also available for blockmaking. Blocks are better contained in boxes or trays to avoid any collapse which may occur, especially when wet. For rockwool systems, the small cubes are inserted in larger cubes or blocks but it is suggested that details of propagation methods or indeed the whole growing system be obtained from the suppliers.

Dark-coloured pots have been shown to absorb solar radiation better than lighter-coloured ones. Plastic pots are also warmer, because they do not lose heat by evaporation.

All pots must be scrupulously clean, especially used clay pots which should be soaked in a solution of formaldehyde (1 in 49) or Jeyes Fluid several weeks prior to using, or alternatively subjected to steaming. The problem of hygiene, coupled with the extra watering necessary, has tended to make clay pots less attractive, but they are nevertheless capable of producing excellent plants.

Peat pots contained in trays on a shallow layer of peat are extremely useful and have a low water requirement. They should always be kept on the dry side, and further apart than other types. Hexagonal paper pots have the advantage of taking up less room, and they can be fitted closer together for brief periods, which is a distinct advantage for light treatment where space is important.

12 & 13 Mineral rockwool propagation – cubes are used from the outset

14 The two sizes of rockwool cube for propagation

Compost for Potting

There is considerable variation in compost type for potting tomatoes, and reference to Chapter 4 will show that the composts used can be (1) John Innes No 1 Potting, (2) soil-less mixes in various proportions, (3) other proprietary or self-formulated types. Much modification has taken place in recent years, not only in the physical nature of the ingredients but in the fertiliser content. Soil-less mixes tend to give softer plants than those grown in John Innes compost. The further north one travels, the smaller the nitrogen requirement in the compost, particularly for early raising, the nitrogen levels appearing to matter less for later raising when light values are higher. Porosity of the compost is important, especially when plants are raised in growing rooms and watered by capillary methods, for which a very rough grit is used in lieu of the more usual mixture of fine and coarse sand.

When rockwool or perlite systems are involved, note that the use of rockwool blocks or compost with a high proportion of perlite should be used.

It is most important to avoid overloading potting media with fertiliser, for this raises the salt content above the acceptable level of pC3: lower pC figures denote higher salt contents.

Potting Procedure (where necessary)

The young plants are teased carefully out of the compost with a clean tally (not pulled out, breaking the root). Each seedling is held by the leaf, with the finger and thumb; avoid handling the stem for this can result in damage to the stem hairs or the actual tissue. Two courses of action can now be employed. The first is to have the pots ready and half filled with the clean, warmed-up compost and, holding the seedling in the centre of the pot with one hand, to press more compost gently into the pot round the seedling with

Fig 25 The correct size and height for pricking off tomato seedlings

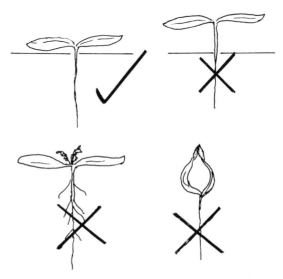

the other, firming and levelling with the fingers. The other method is to fill pots loosely to the brim with compost, then with a finger or dibber make a deep hole in the centre of the pot and carefully insert the seedling, so that the seed leaves are about 1in (2cm) above the top of the compost. The compost is again firmed with the fingers. In both cases the pot is given a sharp tap on the bottom to level up and firm the compost neatly. In the case of soil blocks, seedlings should be very carefully inserted, taking care not to break or bend the root when filling the indent with compost. A light watering is now advisable unless the compost was fairly moist in the first case. (Note the use of tri-sodium ortho-phosphate or disinfectant – *see* p75.)

Plants intended for grafting are generally not potted, but put into boxes (12–24 per box, unless of course they have been space sown in the first case). The procedure is exactly the same as for the second method above: the seed boxes are filled and levelled off, the seedling is inserted with a dibber, firmed and finally watered.

THE CARE OF YOUNG PLANTS

Good light, the correct temperature level and careful watering and feeding are essential if healthy young plants are to be raised. There must also be avoidance of any irregularities that result in checked plants and render them susceptible to parasitic fungal ailments.

Natural light levels must be good for healthy growth, and much can be done to ensure that plants receive all available light by placing them sensibly. With an east–west propagating house this is invariably on the bench running along the south side. An open-slatted bench with warm pipes 9–12in (23–30cm) below the bench is also ideal, although solid benches can give excellent results, and may in fact be a necessity where electrically or pipe warmed benches are being used.

Very popular these days for plant raising are heated propagating cases, which are excellent for tomato plant raising provided they are tall enough to allow the plants to develop. Ideally, however, plants should be slightly hardened off on open benches before being set out in their growing quarters. As the environment in a propagating case tends to produce rather soft plants, it is also important that the propagating case receives sufficient light otherwise the plants can become badly drawn. This is one reason why artificial light has such a valuable role at the plant-raising stage and under very poor, natural light conditions it may be considered desirable to continue with supplementary lighting for a prolonged period, bearing in mind the importance of having the plant-growing quarters ready to cope with the plants when they are available for setting out. The economics of plant raising under artificial light do not usually concern the amateur gardener but commercial growers have found investment in lights and the cost of electricity very well worthwhile.

Temperature Levels
Where the precise control of temperature is possible, it is necessary to decide

on the correct day and night temperatures to have, and there is some difference of opinion on this between northern and southern research establishments, and also between British and European research establishments.

It will be appreciated, from the discussion in Chapter 3, that when light and temperature levels are high and in the absence of any inhibiting factors (such as shortage of CO_2, moisture or nutrients), photosynthesis can generally proceed at an optimum rate. Food manufactured by photosynthetic activity is required by the growing plant, and where it is depressed because of low temperatures and poor light some general debility is unavoidable. This may not be visually apparent, but would affect the formative period of fruit trusses, which are laid down in the plant before they are visible.

Higher day temperatures, with sufficient light intensity, generally increase the rate of growth but reduce the number of flowers on the bottom truss, and this affects the potential number of fruits. High daytime temperatures do in fact induce earlier ripening of the bottom truss, perhaps quite understandably if one assumes that chemical activity proceeds more quickly.

Lower daytime temperatures increase the number of flowers on the bottom truss (and of course the potential number of fruits) but can delay ripening, and there may also be some effect on the viability of the pollen, resulting in poor setting (fertilisation).

The effect of lowering night temperatures is not quite clear, although it is generally accepted that there must be a drop in night temperatures to reduce the respiration of the plant, and so avoid dissipating the available supplies of carbohydrates and protein. Night temperatures must be 'balanced' with day-time temperatures to avoid either an over-supply of carbohydrates (resulting in squat plants) when night temperatures are extremely low, or long leggy plants when night temperatures are too high.

Good light levels are an asset irrespective of temperature levels, although where light levels are poor but daytime temperatures are high there will again be dissipation exhibited by leggy growth, as the plant is unable to manufacture carbohydrates to keep pace with growth rate.

The net result of very low temperatures overall or for prolonged periods will be the production of hard 'blue' plants (*see* p88), which eventually affects fruit production. The possible onset of fungal diseases later in the season due to growth checks cannot be overlooked.

The following table shows temperatures quoted by research authorities for the UK generally, with the lower figures applicable to Scotland.

For the period of propagation, we are concerned with stages (1) and (2). There must usually be some compromise, especially as it is exceedingly doubtful if the degree of precision possible in a highly sophisticated commercial glasshouse unit can be emulated in all spheres of culture, particularly amateur gardening. A fair target, therefore, is about 56–58°F (14°C) at night and 63–65°F (18°C) by day, as far as this is possible, lowering the day temperature a little in very dull weather. Normally, without sophisticated instruments the temperature level tends to drop at night and rise automatically during the day, especially

Recommended Temperatures for Growing Tomatoes						
Stage	Minumum Night		Minimum Day		Ventilation commences at	
	°F	°C	°F	°C	°F	°C
1	59	15	68	20	76	24
2	59	15	64–8	20	74	24
3	56–61	13–16	68	20	79	26
4	56–61	13–16	64	18	70	21

Stage 1: from pricking out the seedlings to the visible appearance of the flower buds in the first truss.

Stage 2: from the first truss flower buds to anthesis (for this purpose the opening of the first flower in that truss).

Stage 3: with the first blooms bursting into colour, the plants are planted out into borders or still in pots and the period extends to four weeks after picking the first ripe fruit.

Stage 4: to end of cropping.

Important note Temperature recommendations are subject to some variation and the above should only be taken as a general guide, particularly as newer varieties tend to have more specific temperature demands.

Note that in the north of the UK, temperature regimes tend to be slightly lower.
Temperatures refer to those accurately recorded by a screened (or at least shaded from a hot sun) thermometer or electric sensor.

if there is high solar radiation. Note that ventilation should take place at 74°F (24°C). A maximum and minimum thermometer is a good investment for checking temperatures.

Different varieties of tomato respond differently to varying temperature ranges, and it is impossible to be very precise about this at the present stage of research. Research work is proceeding on the value of a temporary drop of temperatures, short periods of high temperature and other treatments.

Spacing, Watering, Feeding and Supporting Young Plants

Spacing Young plants must be spaced out as soon as their development demands it, generally three weeks or so after potting and again in another three weeks, and finally a short time before planting out. When plants are congested their leaves are not fully exposed to the light and photosynthesis is reduced, causing plants to become drawn, leggy and etiolated, which raises the height of, and may debilitate, the bottom truss.

Watering There can be no precise ruling on the quantities of water required by young plants. Free-draining compost with a lot of grit requires more water than an all-peat mix. Clay pots dry quickly, paper, plastic and peat less so, indeed there can often be a danger of overwatering peat pots. Nor should peat pots be kept too close together as this encourages them to dry out, and once a soil or peat block is dry it can be very difficult to re-wet it. In any case peat pots and blocks should be separated before inter-rooting takes place as this can give plants a severe check. Continued observation is the only way to gauge a plant's needs, applying water carefully with a long-necked watering-can, or a slow-running hose if a large number of plants are involved, taking pains to avoid saturation or, at the other end of the scale, any wilting of the plants. Research has shown that it apparently makes little difference whether water is at greenhouse temperature or straight from the water supply, although many gardeners prefer to use water from a tank in the greenhouse, provided it is clean and not contaminated with algae or other growths.

Feeding There is some controversy concerning the need to feed plants in pots. Plants in an adequately sized pot in a good John Innes No 1 potting compost could well carry right through to the planting-out stage with no debility. Research workers, however, claim that in this case there will have been a shortage of nutrients causing later debility, which will show up as small fruits on the first or second truss. On balance I feel it is advisable to feed every 10–14 days. Plants in soil-less media should certainly be constantly fed, possibly alternating feeding with plain water to avoid salt concentration buildup, using high potash feeding initially at 1:200, or proprietary feeds at recommended dilutions. Foliar feeding is claimed to be highly advantageous at this stage and it certainly avoids excess salt concentration in the pots. Plants which are propagated later and develop quickly, frequently do not seem to require so much feeding, although I feel that feeding is always desirable with soil-less mixes.

Supporting Plants allowed to flower before planting out will usually require support, generally with a split cane and soft twine.

GUIDE TO RAISING YOUNG PLANTS

The visual appearance of a plant is the only real guide the grower or gardener has regarding its well being, and the table on p88 describes and explains the main points to look for.

GRAFTING

The use of rootstocks is common practice in many spheres of horticulture and involves exploiting the virtues of the rootstocks for the purpose of overcoming inherent weaknesses in the more productive plant grafted on to it. Thus weak varieties of rose are grafted or budded on to vigorous rootstocks, strong varieties of apple are grafted on to weaker rootstocks, and so on. Tomato grafting is intended to utilise the inherent resistance of the rootstock to various maladies which the tomato-fruiting variety itself would be unable to resist. It is therefore possible by this means to grow tomatoes in soil known to be contaminated with certain troubles without resorting to heat or chemical sterilisation, perhaps where sterilisation is not practical for some reason – a situation quite common in both professional and amateur gardening circles.

Symptoms	Cause	Treatment
Pale green plants with long internodes despite regular feeding and good temperature control	Lack of light combined with too high temperatures	Drop day and night temperatures slightly
Yellowing lower leaves, slow growth and poor colour despite regular feeding	Excess watering excluding air from compost which inhibits nutrient uptake	Reduce watering and give an organic stimulant such as dried blood at 2oz/gal (12g/litre)
Spindly, leggy growth despite good colour; burning and shrivelling of leaf tips evident	Excess heat, generally during the day, caused by lack of, or insufficient, ventilation	Ventilate at 70°F (11°C) and damp down frequently; if absent from home all day in hot weather and there is no automatic ventilation, leave vents open to be on the safe side
Dark blue colouration of leaves, especially lower ones, coupled with stocky, hard growth	Excess cold in whole greenhouse, or in one area affected by draughts	Check operation of heating, especially at night, using a maximum and minimum thermometer; put up polythene curtains if necessary to restrict draughts, especially in the region of badly fitting doors
Very dark green plants with excess curling of leaves, yet plants do not grow quickly; shrivelling of leaf edges, especially growing tips	Excess fertiliser or liquid feed being applied, resulting in high salt concentration in the growing medium	Reduce fertiliser or liquid-feed applications, giving a period of plain water to flush out salts
Seed leaves dead and plants look pale or stunted	One or other of the above. The wellbeing of the seed leaves is an excellent barometer of the wellbeing of the plant	Make general check on growing conditions, and use a liquid fertiliser at the correct dilution, if feeding seems necessary.
Leaf mottling, 'blindness' of apical point and growth depression	Unbalanced fertiliser levels or temporary shortage of trace elements	Check feed concentration; minor irregularities usually correct themselves; possibility of weedkiller contamination should not be dismissed
Wilting; general debility or distortion	Fungal or virus disease, or pest attack	See Chapter 11 for full account of pests and diseases, symptoms, preventive and curative measures (if any); in general terms, checks to growth result in development of excess carbohydrates which can readily be plundered by disease pathogens

Rootstock Seed

The rootstocks used are F1 hybrids (which entails raising under controlled conditions) and they are offered by most seed firms as follows (*see* Chapter 11 for details of diseases):

KNVF: corky root, nematodes, verticillium, and fusarium wilt resistance.
TMPVFN (Hires Signal): resistant to mosaic (virus) phytopthora, verticillium, fusarium and nematodes.

Note Certain resistances are now being bred into tomato varieties – see variety list in Chapter 13.

Tomato rootstock seed generally has a harder testa than the fruiting variety and may take longer to germinate, in which case it should be sown (as mentioned on p79) some 4–6 days earlier. Prick off both rootstock and fruiting varieties into trays (or pots) at the density of 12–24 per tray or box. Alternatively sow one seed of each (rootstock and variety) in a pot. Plants should be given plenty of light to encourage strong growth, as grafting can be difficult if they are soft and leggy.

Grafting Procedure

The actual grafting procedure is carried out when plants of both rooting and fruiting varieties are about the same height, about 4–6in (10–15cm) tall, with a stem thickness of $^1/_8$in (3mm), although it is frequently delayed until the plants are taller (this is wise if the grafter is inexperienced). One seedling of both rootstock and fruiting variety is then carefully lifted and, using a sharp clean razor blade, a downward slanting cut is made in the rootstock $^1/_2$–$^3/_4$in (12–20mm) long, and a corresponding upward slanting cut then being made in the fruiting variety. The cut should be made immediately above the area of the seed leaves (which should be removed), taking care not to cut into the stem more than halfway across its diameter, to avoid undue weakening. The two tongues of the cuts are carefully fitted together by one person, while another wraps strips of transparent adhesive cellophane or lead, 1in (2cm) wide, round the stems at the point of the cuts. General procedure is the same if direct sowing into pots has been done.

The *top* leaves of the rootstock are then removed and the plants planted up carefully in pots of $3^1/_2$ – $4^1/_4$in (10–14cm) in diameter. The pots can be closely spaced, usually on an open bench, and they can, if necessary, be draped with polythene to ensure higher humidity than under normal greenhouse conditions; and provided the plants are kept wet but not overwatered, union of the cuts usually occurs fairly quickly, as can readily be seen through the transparent wrapping. Temperature levels are the same as those quoted on p85, and feeding is carried out if necessary.

At planting time it is generally recommended that the fruiting-variety root

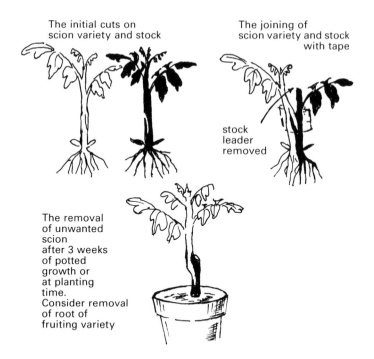

The initial cuts on
scion variety and stock

The joining of
scion variety and stock
with tape

stock
leader
removed

The removal
of unwanted
scion
after 3 weeks
of potted
growth or
at planting
time.
Consider removal
of root of
fruiting variety

Fig 26 Tomato grafting

is removed immediately below the graft in order to avoid the possible later transmission of fungal vascular infection to which this root is susceptible, but personal experience shows that a cultural check is caused by this procedure. In fact the fruiting-plant root generally withers in time, and is then unlikely to transmit vascular diseases. In any case the remaining upper portion of the rootstock should be cleanly removed. Suckers will inevitably form at ground level and should also be removed regularly.

One vital point on the technique of grafting is hygiene during the grafting procedure; it is relatively simple to infect the cuts with disease unless the blade is dipped frequently in a solution of 2 per cent tri-sodium ortho-phosphate or disinfectant.

While grafted plants are slow to establish when planted, they develop considerable vigour which invariably continues well into the autumn.

Note The whole matter of tomato grafting must be given careful consideration with regard to the resistances now being introduced into tomato varieties. The success of certain alternative cultural systems also throws doubt on the economic viability of grafting. Nevertheless, it is a technique of considerable value for gardeners wishing to grow plants in unsterilised borders without all the problems of watering and feeding which can be encountered in most other systems. It is a system not lavishly advertised because it does not involve the sale of compost, growbags or other accoutrements. The same can be said about straw-bale culture (*see* Chapter 6).

6

An Examination of
Cultural Methods

The actual physical growth of a tomato plant from the time of seed germination to its ultimate demise could be said, botanically speaking, to follow a fairly consistent pattern. Yet there are so many variables to take into account and so many ways of achieving the same results that confusion inevitably arises in the mind of the gardener or grower. There can obviously be no 'best' way of growing tomatoes under all the differing conditions, nor indeed are the results entirely consistent, owing to differences in the weather from season to season, or perhaps the progressive onset of disease under particular cultural conditions.

I feel that in previous chapters of this book there has been a sufficiently detailed account of the different circumstances and situations under which tomatoes may be grown for the grower to be able to gauge the level of success she or he is likely to achieve. Under good natural light conditions, with a well-sited greenhouse of good design, with adequate ventilation and a good level of heating, and where the correct environment can be maintained and supplies of water and nutrients controlled to fine limits, then one would expect, given a good pest- and disease-free medium in which to grow the plants, that success is inevitable. Yet to dwell completely in the realms of such a tomato-growing Utopia would, I feel, be unrealistic, certainly for the greater proportion of those who read this book. It is certainly commendable to strive for the ideal, yet in the course of a great many years' advisory work (combined with the culture of tomatoes on my own account), I can seldom recall a situation where every cultural requirement to the present level of knowledge was completely and absolutely fulfilled.

With tomato culture, perhaps more than with the culture of any other crop, there is always something new to learn or something new to try. The very fact that so many cultural methods exist proves this point adequately.

What can be a problem, especially for the commercial grower, is keeping abreast with new systems for growing tomatoes. Even in ordinary gardening spheres there is much happening, and the really keen gardeners may wonder if they are not missing out on some highly successful technique. It has, however, been stressed before that commercial firms are unwilling to release a system on to the market until it is really foolproof, especially in the hands of amateur gardeners.

'Balance Sheet' of Growing Methods
Conventional Border Culture

The tomatoes are grown in the soil forming the 'floor' or border of the greenhouse.

Credit	Debit
A fairly stable water and nutrient regime related to water tables of the area. Less water loss than from containers or bales. A border retains moisture effectively, an advantage during absence at business or on holiday. Border growing, with the addition of compost trenches, is a system which will suit the organic enthusiast, provided there can be a sufficiently long rotation to avoid buildup of pests and diseases, although, conversely, there may be those who are quite prepared to remove and replace compost.	During wet weather water may seep into the border, causing chilling and excluding air, this being a serious possibility in the early months of the year, and especially detrimental then. It is not always possible to control the quantity of moisture available. Soil is slow to warm up, frequently resulting in planting checks, with serious long-term repercussions such as root rot, wilt, eelworm attack etc. Conventional culture without sterilisation (and even with it in certain cases) can result in problems due to the buildup of pests, such as potato cyst eelworm, and diseases (see Chapter 11). Salts (fertiliser residues) and plant acids will also accumulate in the soil. Excess vigour of plants can be difficult to control, especially in freshly sterilised soil-containing media. Resoiling is laborious and it may be difficult to obtain reliable soil entirely free from weeds, diseases and pests.

Border Culture using Grafted Plants

Credit	Debit
The same advantages as are mentioned in the entry relating to conventional border culture, coupled with the ability of the existing rootstock (because of their inbred resistance) to grow well despite the presence of several serious maladies, thus avoiding the need to sterilise the soil. Some of these resistances have now been conferred to fruiting varieties grown normally on their own roots. Plants maintain good vigour right to the end of the season.	The technique of grafting can be tedious and if the plants are to be bought they can be difficult and costly to obtain. Specific inherent resistances have a bad habit of breaking down, but the plant breeder is usually able to take the necessary action. Virus disease may be spread by the grafting process. Fruit is usually slightly later in ripening. Vigorous roots may contact deep-seated virus infection in soil.

Ring Culture

Plants are grown in compost in 9in (22cm) bottomless bituminised paper pots or other similar-sized containers, which are planted on a 4–6in (10–15cm) layer of porous and inert material such as grit, weathered ashes or gravel.

Credit	Debit
Only relatively small quantities of pest- and disease-free growing media are required, renewed annually, ensuring a good start. The growing medium warms up quickly as it is freely exposed to both heat from the sun and artificial heat (it also cools quickly). Excellent control of vigour can be exercised by early root restriction. This results generally in fruit production of a high order. Deep-seated pest and disease problems are normally of no consequence.	Watering and feeding must be constant and carried out with considerable precision. Water loss is very high, especially in hot weather, and early drying out can have serious consequences, especially later in the season, as root damage may ensue. Setting aside a section of the greenhouse for ring culture tends to limit its use for crops such as chrysanthemums, although they can be grown in ring culture. Salt buildup (fertiliser residues) can be a serious problem in the limited quantity of growing media.

Straw-bale Culture

Plants are grown in a ridge of growing medium on straw bales or wads which have been induced by chemical treatment to ferment, which generates heat. Straw-bale culture using organic liquid feeds such as seaweed-based Maxicrop (to induce fermentation) is much favoured by organic growers. Polythene lined trenches filled with straw can also be used.

Credit	Debit
Warmth at the roots is ensured, resulting in excellent development. As with ring culture, a 'clean' start is ensured. CO_2 enrichment by decomposition of straw is beneficial to plants.	Vast quantities of water are essential, both initially to soak the bales, and throughout the season. Bales are heavy and bulky, taking up a lot of room, although sections of bales can be used. Vigour control can be difficult as root development is uninhibited and uncontrollable supplies of nitrogen are released from the decomposing straw. Deficiency of nitrogen can also occur, especially early in the season. *Risk of weedkiller residues.*

Container and Substrate Culture

A number of systems can be included under this broad heading, involving growing plants in whalehide pots, in bolsters or other containers or bags. Basically speaking, they all involve isolation from doubtful greenhouse borders so that plants are not infested or infected with pests and diseases from the borders. A description of these systems in broad terms follows; note that there is an overlap between various systems.

1. Polythene bags Plants are grown in soil-less media in large black polythene bags, set in a layer of polythene which acts as a barrier to pests and diseases, or on layers of free-draining aggregate.

2. Peat mattress system 9in (22cm) whalehide pots are set in a trough of polythene on a 2–3in (5–7cm) layer of peat.

Growing in border soil
– traditional method,
losing popularity

Ring culture – growing in
9in (23cm) rings placed on
4in (10cm) of ash or gravel

Straw-bale culture –
popular in 1960s before
advent of bolsters

Peat growbags – popular
with both amateurs and
professionals

Nutrient film culture –
growing in a shallow
film of nutrient solution
in a trough

Rockwool and perlite
bolsters – favoured by
professionals as an
alternative to peat growbags

Fig 27 Different ways of growing tomatoes

3. Various containers Bolsters/growbags (polythene bags with the tops opened up); buckets (with drainage holes); boxes, trays or troughs constructed of wood, polythene or other material.

Credit	Debit
A pest- and disease-free start in relatively small quantities of growing media. Root growth and vigour are usually excellent.	Watering and feeding require considerable precision. Surplus water shed from bags can result in soggy soil and raise the humidity. A salt problem can frequently occur in the medium, resulting in 'black bottoms' (*see* p171) and other troubles.

Hydroponics

Various systems of culture involve growing plants in nutrient solutions or 'inert' substrates such as rockwool or perlite, as distinct from using soil or peat-based composts. Some hydroponic systems are simple, as is the case when growing in sand, gravel or other aggregate. The most advanced system is called the nutrient film technique (NFT), when plants are grown in shallow layers of nutrient, in sloping polythene troughs, this being a system much favoured by commercial growers (*see* Appendix 3, p190).

15 *Tomatoes on straw bales in the author's greenhouse*

16 *Nutrient film technique (NFT) systems of culture are widely used in commercial spheres*

Credit	Debit
A clean start is ensured and by means of strict nutrient control very large crops can be produced.	On some systems, notably NFT, spread of disease from plant to plant can be rapid. With other systems, plants are more isolated. Very precise control is necessary of the nutrient balance. In general, hydroponic systems are not for the hit or miss gardener.

SOME ASPECTS OF WATER APPLICATION IN TOMATO CULTURE

Water is the life blood of all plants, and when they are grown under glass the only source available to them apart from reserves in the ground where border culture is involved, is what is applied by the grower or gardener, though a certain amount of water can travel laterally from outside sources and there can be seepage from moisture shed from the roof of the greenhouse. Where cultural systems other than border culture are concerned all water must be supplied artificially. The application of water is best considered according to the different categories.

Winter Flooding in Border Culture

The need to flood out surplus fertilisers and top up the moisture reserves in the soil is frequently emphasised in connection with the border culture of tomatoes. It is usually done some weeks prior to planting, and where steam sterilisation has been carried out: it follows immediately on this to wash out surplus ammonia. Research has shown, however, that apart from chilling the border, excess quantities of water may do much harm by causing damage to soil structure. It is now usual in commercial circles to have the soil analysed to ascertain the soluble salt content, and to use this as a guide as to whether or not flooding is necessary. Generally speaking, it is advisable to give the borders a reasonably heavy watering two weeks or so prior to planting to avoid their drying out. Where soil analysis shows the need for a thorough flooding, heavy soils will require much more than light soils, the following table being a rough guide:

Area of border		Light soil		Heavy soil	
sq yd	m^2	gal	litres	gal	litres
10	10	40	53	80	424
20	20	80	106	160	850
30	30	120	160	240	1,272
40	40	160	212	320	1,700
80	80	320	424	640	3,392

For larger areas, multiply accordingly. Where soils merely need pre-planting watering, around a quarter of the quantities stated should suffice. Note that these are only 'guide' figures.

Ailsa Craig, probably the best-known tomato variety, and still superb quality

Sweet 100, superb for children, and adults

(*left*) Gardener's Delight, a winner for those who like small tomatoes

Grenadier, a long-established tomato, still in demand

(*right*) Alicante, highly popular for its superb quality and colour

Tornado, a good compact outdoor variety

(*right*) Dona, a beefsteak tomato, new in 1988, and resistant to disease

Golden Sunrise, one of the oldest and most reliable yellow varieties

Flooding should always be carried out in 'mist' form with either a rose on the end of a hosepipe or spraylines, to keep damage to soil structure to a minimum. The amount of water delivered can be measured either by meter or, on a smaller scale, by sample collection in a bucket or other receptacle where spraylines are being used. For example, if a square biscuit tin of 1sq ft ($900cm^2$) surface area is put down and collects 1gal (4.5litres) of water in 2 minutes then, provided the distribution of water from the spraylines is even over the whole area, a brief calculation will quickly determine the total quantity delivered.

Commercial growers may decide to have the salt content of their soil checked after flooding to see that it has been reduced to a 'safe' level.

Hygiene

Washing down houses inside and out is a practice which requires water of suitable pressure to be delivered from the end of a hose so that it can be directed at the glass and into corners. Washing down must fit in conveniently with the cropping plans for the greenhouse. Obviously it should be carried out before sterilisation. Prior to washing down, a mild detergent can be brushed on to the glass structure with a long-handled brush.

Damping down and Pollination

(See also p45). Water in fine mist form is used for the purpose of raising humidity in the greenhouse so that pollen grains do not dry out and prevent 'setting', no matter what system of culture is involved, although some by their very nature do create high humidity, straw bales being typical in this respect. One effect of too dry an atmosphere is 'dry set' (see p172). Damping down raises the humidity and also reduces the transpiration of the plant, and this is very important during their establishment period.

The actual shaking of the plants for the purpose of moving the pollen from anther to stigma is generally carried out either with sprinkler lines or, more usual on a smaller scale, with hosepipes fitted with a rose, cane tapping or vibrators.

When plants are young, and especially when grown in borders, they can readily be watered overhead, their water requirements being small; this serves also for damping down. When plants are taller, however, damping down is then carried out briefly for a few minutes, generally at mid-morning on a sunny day, the vents being shut to raise the humidity for between 30 and 45 minutes. The actual watering of established plants, on the other hand, is carried out according to the plants' needs, estimated either by visual assessment or by other more precise methods now in use.

Assessing Water Requirements

While visual assessment will obviously suffice for a small number of plants, it is desirable to use more accurate ways of determining water needs for tomatoes grown on a larger scale. Tensiometers or moisture meters, for example, record the osmotic pressure of the soil – which can be related to a water-requirement table – or, more simply, with border or ring culture, state whether the soil is wet, medium or dry. Tensiometers are effective in soil-less media also. Various systems of calculating water needs, some computerised and highly sophisticated, are now widely used commercially. New systems are coming out all the time especially with the many methods now used for actually applying water and liquid foods to the plants. Having said this, the majority of gardeners still rely on visual assessment. For those who want things more precisely, there are meters which can measure the amount of water delivered through a standpipe. *Small moisture meters are very helpful, and inexpensive too.*

Another way of assessing water needs is to refer to tables used initially by the Fairfield Experimental Station in Lancashire (now closed). A healthy tomato plant will, on average, take upwards of 22 gal (100 litres) of water in the full growing season (excluding propagation). This is the quantity required by the plant and does not take into account drainage loss and surface evaporation. The figures apply to plants over 3ft (1m) tall; adjustments must be made for smaller plants.

The actual requirement ranges from $1^3/_4$ pints (1 litre) per week to nearly 3 gal (14 litres), a fair average being 2 gal (10 litres) per week, giving a total of 44 gal (200 litres) – it can be seen what percentage of water is lost by drainage and surface evaporation, especially as even more water than this may have to be given. Plants on ring culture could in fact require considerably more water, owing to the porous nature of the aggregate. The same is true of other cultural systems, especially straw-bale or bolster, and there is no real substitute for practical experience of any method. The table below gives an indication of the likely requirements.

Weather pattern	Water requirement by plant for full 24hr day	
	pints	litres
Very dull – cloudy and dull most of the day	$1/_4$–$1/_2$	0.14–0.28
Dull – overcast most of the day	$1/_2$–$3/_4$	0.28–0.42
Fairly sunny – cloudy with bright periods	$1^1/_4$–$1^1/_2$	0.71–0.85
Sunny – only occasional cloud	2–$2^1/_4$	1.1–1.2
Very sunny – sky clear and sunny all day	3–$3^1/_4$	1.5–1.8

It cannot be stressed too strongly that, with new systems of culture being introduced, quantities of water application require constant reappraisal, especially where systems such as NFT are involved. Nevertheless, the water loss of plants does appear to remain reasonably constant. A distorting factor must be the longer growing season now practised by the specialist tomato grower. In the main, however, these considerations do not affect the smaller-scale grower or amateur gardener.

The use of floor liner (*see* p40) will also affect watering in some systems.

7
Pre-planting Procedures

It has earlier been agreed (*see* Chapter 3) that the development of the tomato plant, from seed to its continued production of fruit, follows, throughout the season and physiologically speaking, a basically similar pattern no matter what the system of culture or district. This of course can be said about any plant; it is the ability to maximise production, both in respect of total weight and of quality, which brings more sophisticated aspects of culture into play.

While there may be 'secrets' involved in tomato culture which will coax the plant to give of its best, I feel that it is more valid to consider tomato growing as a reasonably precise science.

SELECTION OF CULTURAL METHOD

The decision to grow tomatoes by one or other of the methods previously alluded to need not necessarily entail great deliberation. There should first of all be a critical review of last season's results and, if possible at the end of the season, a close examination of the spent plants, especially their root systems. Detailed pathological and entomological guidance is given in Chapter 11, but the following is a general approach to the subject.

Where plants have cropped well and can be removed with a fairly extensive amount of healthy-looking, white root which is still more or less physically intact, then it can be assumed that conditions have been good and there has been little incidence of pests or disease. This sort of situation is common in a 'new' soil for the first year of cropping when border growing.

Where the plants have cropped fairly well, yet only a small portion of their root system remains and most of this breaks away on lifting, it can be taken as reasonable evidence of the presence of soil-borne maladies, especially if the remaining root is brown and rotted. This indicates the probable buildup of these troubles in future to proportions that will affect the ensuing crop seriously, unless evasive action is taken. There appears to be hardly any enthusiasm in specialist commercial spheres for border growing.

Complete collapse of a high proportion of the plants during the season is usually indicative of serious troubles – unless only stems or leaves of plants are attacked – demanding, with border cultivation, sterilisation, re-soiling or alternative cultural methods. Whether the soil was new or sterilised before cropping, the presence of troubles shows that pests and diseases were involved and this is the important issue when deciding on cultural methods for the next crop. Indeed, it is this sort of situation which has led to the popularity of growbags or other systems as these ensure that a new start can be made each year, without worrying about sterilisation of soil or other issues where the border soil is in doubt. (There may in fact be no suitable soil in the greenhouse border in the first case, a common situation these days when greenhouses may be built on newly levelled sites, in a convenient spot where there is no soil. The main considerations may well have been only the site of the greenhouse, light, services and access.)

It must be pointed out that the use of growbags is merely one alternative method of culture, albeit a very convenient one much publicised by the major suppliers in a modern garden centre. As referred to earlier, there are other equally effective systems, such as straw bales, ring culture or for that matter grafted plants, which do not involve high labour or high cost. Having said this, while the commercial grower must concern himself with costs and returns, the same is not true of the hobby gardener. Indeed, in many instances of hobby gardening, such as tomato growing, actual cost of production may well exceed the value of the produce but the important issues are the fun of growing, the sense of satisfaction, and the availability of fresh, newly picked fruit for the salad bowl.

BORDER CULTIVATION – PRELIMINARY CONSIDERATIONS

The use of the greenhouse border or 'floor' is still a reasonably common form of culture, especially when using grafted tomato plants or adopting organic growing methods. It seems likely, too, that tomato varieties with inbred resistance to root and vascular problems will, in time, become more widely used than at present. The physical issues, such as drainage, even soil depth or lack of subsoil pan, are important, and it is well worth taking the time and trouble to dig a few inspection holes to check on the subsoil and the even distribution of the topsoil, especially if levelling has taken place recently or at some time. Water should also be allowed to run into an inspection hole to see how long it takes to drain away, in order to confirm that drainage is adequate. Further investigation should also be made to see if seepage from outside the greenhouse, or water runoff from roofs or higher land, is likely to be a problem. This is something which is frequently ignored, but which can give rise to considerable trouble, especially for early crops.

If the soil itself is of good physical quality, this gives a flying start although much can be done to improve soil in a limited area by adding peat.

Presumably border culture will only be considered where the soil is new to tomatoes or has been effectively sterilised. Potato cyst eelworm is the only really serious long-term malady likely to be a hazard to border cultivation in a 'new' soil. It should be realised that potato eelworm, affecting as it does solanaceous plants, to which family tomatoes and potatoes belong, is likely to arise mainly from continuous potato cropping, whether by the gardener or as a legacy from farming days. Eelworm can also readily be carried in on feet or by water, and can be blown in from neighbouring land.

Soil analysis and eelworm counts are, I feel, essential preliminaries to border cultivation, on any scale.

Isolation of the greenhouse border soil from outside infestation, especially in respect of eelworm, is something which should be given serious consideration, although if the greenhouse foundation is fairly deep, this should suffice. More important for older borders will be the problems of deep-seated 'self-inflicted' troubles – root rots, potato cyst eelworm and virus diseases from previous tomato crops – *which are difficult or impossible to control completely even with sterilisation.*

There are problems in installing barriers of either polythene or concrete, not the least of which is drainage and, to be practical, it is better to consider methods other than border culture rather than going to these lengths.

Preparing the Soil for Border Cultivation

In theoretical terms all that is necessary is to provide the tomato with air, moisture and soluble nutrients and it will produce crops. I have seen excellent crops grown on this premise, both in Britain and on the Continent, especially in the Netherlands, Spain or Middle Eastern countries where tomatoes are grown on many of the reclaimed coastal or arid areas in almost pure sand. Yet there is obviously great virtue in growing a crop in a soil of good structure, where air penetration, moisture movement and nutrient release are optimal compared with a 'played out' soil where the structure has been destroyed or has deteriorated and the mineral particles, instead of existing in crumbs, are packed together. The fashion in which nutrients are released is also thought to contribute to the quality of the tomato fruit, and this indeed adds considerably to the quality of tomatoes grown in heavy northern soils, although slightly lower growing temperatures and a longer period of fruit formation cannot be ignored as one of the main reasons for this. Organic growing also provides excellent quality fruit.

While, on a larger scale, rotary cultivation or ploughing may be the desirable method of cultivating the soil, digging is much more likely to be the method favoured by the majority of smaller growers and gardeners. The reason for digging a soil at all is not perhaps fully understood, it often being carried out by sheer habit. The virtues of digging are best listed as:

1 Loosening of the soil and physically creating air and moisture channels
2 Allowing the ready incorporation of bulky organic humus or 'conditioners'
3 In deep digging, improving drainage by loosening the subsoil
4 Allowing easy planting in the loosened soil
5 Inverting the soil, if digging is correctly executed, ie bringing up the lower area to the top and vice versa, which in theory should bring nutrient-containing soil to the area of early root development; subsoil should be left where it is
6 Allowing weeds and surface debris to be put below the top spit of soil to act as a source of organic matter.

Digging should be carried out during December or January, or before

Cultural Method Selection and Crop Timing				
Condition of border soil and performance of previous crop (if any)	*Condition of roots of previous crop*	*Heat and light levels*	*Control of environment and feeding*	*Advised cultural methods*
Soil good, 'new' soil or ground rested before being compost dressed. No great danger of seepage. Previous crop performance good.	Good	Good	Good	Border culture: early or second early crop. Sterilisation not essential but advisable for second crop as safety measure unless organic methods practised.
Soil good, previous crop performance fairly good and pre-planting sterilisation carried out, or alternatively re-soiled.	Fair	Fair	Fair	Border culture for mid-season crop only. Sterilisation desirable, or adopt organic methods.
Soil doubtful. Performance variable. Sterilisation, organic growing or re-soiling impractical.	Poor	Good	Fair	Avoid border crop culture with conventional varieties: use of grafted plants is a reasonable alternative at lower cropping levels. Consider other cultural systems.
Soil good. Previous crop performed reasonably well. Sterilisation impractical.	Fair	Poor	Fair	Border culture for mid-season crop only. Grafted plants could be used but problems of growth in areas of poor light indicate container or straw-bale culture for earlier crops.
Soil poor. Cropping results poor or complete failure.	Very poor	Poor	Poor	Grow on ring culture, straw-bales, containers etc; cold or mildly heated crop only.

mid-November if chemical sterilisation is being carried out (*see* Chapter 12). Whether deep or double digging is preferable to single digging is now perhaps the subject of some controversy. The roots of tomatoes are capable of growing to a great depth, as determined by underground observation windows at experimental stations. Yet deep roots remain in the soil and can result in the buildup of deep-seated troubles, especially virus diseases, despite sterilisation – which is generally only effective to a depth of 10–12in (25–30cm). The philosophy of digging only to shallow depths to discourage deep rooting (provided drainage is in no way inhibited) could have certain merits, especially as tomato plants can produce excellent crops in relatively small quantities of growing medium, as will be seen later.

During digging, any vegetative portions of noxious weeds should of course be removed, especially where couch grass or horsetail exist, as can often be the case in a 'new' soil. The same is true of tree roots which can present a considerable hazard to crops growing in greenhouse borders, especially tomatoes which make heavy demands on moisture and nutrient reserves. This raises the point that some control measures outside the greenhouse will also be necessary to prevent re-introduction. A word of warning here: do not use very soluble types of weedkiller such as sodium chlorate immediately outside a greenhouse, as this can readily seep through into the greenhouse soil. It is much safer to use weed-control methods based on 'spot' application with weedkillers such as Tumbleweed or other systemic types actually absorbed by the plant leaves.

The Case for Applying Organic Materials

Farmyard manure (FYM) When applying any type of organic matter there are two basic considerations. Some types of organic matter contain fair quantities of nutrients (*see* p51) while others do not. To apply FYM is to provide a source of nutrients and at the same time physically to condition the soil – physically in the sense that the sheer bulk of FYM separates the soil particles and creates channels for air and moisture movement. The 'conditioning' is done by providing the raw material for humus production with all the benefits which this entails, crumb formation of the soil particles being of primary importance.

Peat, a very popular form of organic matter these days, merely conditions the soil and does not supply any appreciable quantities of readily available nutrients. Yet this can be a very great advantage, as one has all the benefits of conditioning without the complications of applying unknown quantities of nutrients, which after all can be much more accurately applied in fertiliser form.

A still further complication is that where FYM is applied, an excessive amount of nitrogen may be made available to the plant, particularly if heat sterilisation has been practised, and there will be a rapid production of ammonia.

Well-rotted FYM should be applied at rates of up to 1 ton per 108–110sq yd or 1cwt per 8–19sq yd (50kg/9m^2). FYM can also contain weeds, pests and diseases, not to mention disinfectants. Wood shavings are often used in the bedding of animals these days, and if these are present in quantity they can give rise to some nutritional problems, such as temporary nitrogen shortage.

Municipal compost Municipal compost is freely available in many districts and can be used at rates of up to one-sixth of the total bulk of soil. It can, however, contain quantities of heavy metals and so give rise to nutritional problems on a long-term basis.

Peat Peat can be used copiously at the same rate as FYM (about 10lb/4kg or more per sq yd/m²), although it is frequently used less lavishly than this. Note that sphagnum peat is very acid and that where it is applied in quantity there will be a considerable lowering of the pH figure. To offset this, for every bushel (36 litres) of peat allows 5–6oz (170g) of ground limestone.

Other organic materials The application of materials such as garden compost or weathered spent mushroom compost is also useful for soil-conditioning purposes, although unless garden compost is properly made it can be very suspect. At the risk of offending organic gardening enthusiasts, let me hasten to add that properly prepared garden compost is a truly excellent material for applying to tomato borders and will result in fruit of a superlative quality. It is generally applied in trenches or holes taken out of the greenhouse border. There are no upper limits to the quantities necessary, supply usually being the main problem. One word of warning, however, concerning the organic method of growing tomatoes: when pests or diseases are inadvertently introduced there may be a 'wait period' before natural balance is restored, and this could result in very serious crop loss. Straw-bale culture is a highly acceptable alternative. Gardeners anxious to know more about composting principles are advised to get in touch with the Soil Association or other organic-growing bodies (*see* Appendix 4).

Topping up the Water Reservoir and Flooding

After cultivation of the border, consideration must be given to the need for topping up the water reservoir, and flooding to wash out excess salts along with plant toxins – especially following steam sterilisation. There has already been discussion on this point in Chapter 6 and broadly speaking the following rules should be observed:

1 Where soil is new, or re-soiling has taken place, merely water to moisten the soil well 2 to 3 weeks before planting.
2 Where soil has been sterilised by heat, flood to wash out surplus ammonia 2 to 3 weeks before planting.
3 Where soil has been used for some years and is chemically sterilised, check salt content to ascertain whether flooding is necessary. If flooding is not necessary, merely water before planting.

When methods other than border culture are to be carried out, flooding does not have to be considered: the water is simply given to the growing plant as it needs it.

Application of Lime

Soil analysis will determine the pH figure and also give a lime requirement. Ideally tomatoes in a soil-based medium like a pH figure of 6.5. Lime can be applied after any flooding, or lightly washed in near the end of the flooding period. There is a tendency these days to use magnesian limestone (Dolomitic limestone), which contains magnesium as well as calcium, but ground limestone can of course also be used. Where analysis is not carried out, it is necessary to guess how much lime is required, and 8oz of ground lime per sq yd ($260g/m^2$) is a normal application for soil, although it would be better to check the pH figure. Lime should be applied evenly, and if not lightly watered in it should be forked in. The problem of contact between any lime and FYM which has been applied, with the subsequent release of ammonia, always exists. If, however, the FYM has been well turned in, there is little immediate physical contact and therefore little danger. Nor in fact is there any real danger of ammonia release if either ground or magnesian limestone is used, as neither of these materials is caustic, whereas hydrated lime is relatively so.

Ammonia release in gaseous form will of course damage any seeds or plants in the vicinity and also result in loss of nitrogen. There is also the further danger that, if the ammonia is dissolved in the soil water, it will be taken up by the plant, causing very rank growth, if not more severe long- or short-term damage. Where organic-growing principles apply and considerable quantities of well made compost are used in trenches or for top dressing, lime is not generally necessary unless the soil or compost is shown to be very acid.

APPLICATION OF BASE NUTRIENTS

While fairly precise rules exist for the application of base nutrients to tomatoes, it should be pointed out again that it is often very difficult to make accurate allowances for the nutrient reserves in the soil (*see also* p64). Many experiments have been carried out where no base applications at all were given to older tomato soils, the nutrient requirements of the plants being met as they grew. There is increasing favour of such procedure, even for new low-nutrient soils and media, with liquid feed being applied from the outset. It is, unfortunately, not possible to state which method is preferable or which will give greater success.

Soil analysis, despite its failings, will at least give an indication of the existing nutrient level of the borders, and it will in its more sophisticated forms certainly provide an accurate soluble-salt figure. Where salt contents are found by analysis to be of a high order and where flooding cannot be carried out, then obviously the application of most base dressings would be folly, as this would put the salt content at danger level. Conversely when soil analysis shows the soluble-salt content to be low and nutrient levels fairly high, some base dressings should be applied to bring the salt content to a level which will exercise growth control by evening up the osmotic pressures. Nutrient applications (N, P, K) can, in this instance, be waived, and only magnesium sulphate applied, as the adjusting agent.

Base Nutrient Application Procedures			
Soil	Nutrient level as confirmed by analysis	Level of Soluble salts	Advised course of action
Old tomato soil	Medium to high	Normal	Apply either no base at all, feeding the plants with liquid feed (at correct dilution) from outset or apply base dressing or magnesium to bring salt content to a pC of 2.8.
Old tomato soil	Medium to high	High	Try to flood if possible, but if not, apply no base feed. Liquid feed from outset according to appearance of plants.
'New' tomato soil	Low	Low	Apply base dressing, including magnesium sulphate, at full rate.
Old tomato soil	Medium to high	Low	Apply only magnesium sulphate, to adjust soluble salt content.

Types of Base Dressing

Tomato base feeds are available with 'high potash', 'medium potash' and 'high nitrogen' contents. High-potash bases are applied following steam sterilisation, the extra potash being included to counteract the excess nitrogen produced after the sterilising procedure. Medium-potash base dressings are for soils which have either been sterilised chemically or not sterilised at all. High-nitrogen base dressings are applied when nitrogen levels are likely to be low, for example following a lettuce crop or perhaps when planting very late. It will be noted that considerable importance is placed on the nitrogen/potash ratio, the phosphorus levels being more or less ignored.

Typical base-feed dressings are given below. The John Innes base is frequently used as a high-potash base, but tends to be expensive. Very early tomato growers frequently apply additional sulphate of potash and it is now standard practice to apply magnesium sulphate in addition for both early and late crops.

Quantities of Base Dressing to Apply

While soil analysis can be used as a practical guide, the more important considerations have already been outlined. The normal rate of base dressing can be reduced to 6oz per sq yd (200g/m²) when applying 3oz (85g) sulphate of potash. Magnesium sulphate is also applied at 3oz per sq yd (100g/m²) provided there is no salt problem.

For main-crop (as distinct from early) tomatoes apply less potash (2oz or 66g/m²), while for late tomatoes it is doubtful whether extra sulphate of potash should be applied at all, but the base fertiliser applications can be pushed up to 8oz (264g/m²) on heat-sterilised soils. Vigorous varieties may require high-potash base feeds under all circumstances.

Base feeds, carefully measured out, must be applied evenly, as concentrations in any one area will give rise to salt problems which could be serious if plant positions happen to coincide with such areas.

Base Dressing Types and Quantities				
Crop	Soil	Base type	Quantity	
			oz/sq yd	g/m²
Early and main crop tomatoes	Sterilised	High-potash base	6	200
		Sulphate of potash	2–3	68–100
		*Magnesium sulphate	3	100
Early and main	Not sterilised or chemically sterilised	Medium-potash base	8	270
		*Magnesium sulphate	3	100
Late tomatoes (either heated or cold grown)	Heat sterilised	High-potash base	8	270
		*Magneisum sulphate	3	100
Late tomatoes (either heated or cold grown)	Unsterilised or chemically sterilised	Medium-potash base	6	200
		*Magnesium sulphate	3	100

*Do not apply magnesium sulphate if there is a high soluble-salt problem and flooding is not practicable. Modifications to these quantities may be needed for vigorous or weak varieties. Apply high-nitrogen base feeds at 6oz per sq yd (200g/m²) following lettuce or other nitrogen-demanding crop.

Final Preparations

Normally the condition of the soil in greenhouse borders following cultivation and any flooding necessary is sufficiently good to allow base fertilisers to be applied before finally forking down the bed preparatory to planting. A light forking, followed perhaps by some consolidation to get rid of any lumps, and finally raking down to produce a reasonably level and fine tilth, should be carried out, though it is unnecessary to go to extreme lengths. Consider use of floor liner.

Pre-planting Timetable for Border Cultivation	
What to do	*When to do it*
1. An assessment of the previous crop performance and examination of rooting system to determine the best course of action for the next crop, including the need for sterilisation.	Oct–Nov
Chemically sterilise with metham-sodium if necessary. (*See* Chapter 13 for further details on sterilisation.)	Before 15 Nov
2. Soil analysis and eelworm cyst count, paying particular attention to soluble salt level.	November
3. Cultivation, including weed removal and subsoil loosening.	December
4. Complementary to cultivation will be the incorporation of organic matter such as FYM, peat and compost.	December
5. Flooding, if necessary or deemed advisable.	Jan–March
6. Lime application if necessary according to pH and lime-requirement figure.	Jan–March
7. Pre-planting watering if borders are too dry.	Jan–March
8. Application of base dressings 7–10 days before planting.	Feb–May
9. Forking of bed, consolidation, and raking of soil reasonably level.	Feb–May
10. Consideration of whether to put a floor liner of black-white polythene (white upwards) over the whole border before or after planting.	

GROWING GRAFTED TOMATOES – INITIAL PREPARATIONS

There is no difference in soil preparation, apart from the obvious fact that there is no need for sterilisation. There could be instances, however, where sterilisation is still worthwhile even when grafted plants are used, especially if the soil is very weedy; this matter is dealt with in Chapter 12.

RING CULTURE – INITIAL PREPARATIONS

Ring culture is a method of growing tomatoes in a growing medium in quantities which allow for complete renewal annually without great labour or expense. The two-zone rooting system, with the initial surface roots in the rings and, as the season progresses, a 'take-over' by roots which develop in the aggregate, allows a considerable measure of growth control difficult to achieve where roots are allowed to develop freely under the uninhibited conditions of border growing. These issues will become clearer as the cultural directions are discussed in more detail.

The 'clean' start that can be made with ring culture demands a hygienic approach from the outset. The existing border soil (if any exists in the first case) should be removed to a depth of 6–8in (15–20cm) or more to make way for a

6in (15cm) layer of aggregate, below which there should be ample provision for good drainage, and this could mean laying down some tile drains. As ring culture is usually adopted because of a history of crop failures, merely to put the aggregate on top of the remaining soil is obviously to leave the way open for further pest or disease problems, unless the existing soil can be isolated effectively. Potato cyst eelworm is the main culprit, although there could also be viral diseases harboured in the root debris of earlier tomato crops. The more common fungal parasites are not likely to be such a problem, as they tend to exist largely in the top layer of soil. One therefore has to decide whether to lay down a floor of concrete or to use a polythene barrier, in both instances ensuring that drainage is not inhibited.

Whether or not to sterilise the lower level of soil chemically is open to controversy, but is generally not advisable. Subsoil of poor quality frequently lacks texture, making the dissipation of chemical soil sterilants difficult. Sterilisation should perhaps be confined to washing down the lower foundations of the greenhouse with formaldehyde (1 in 49). A deeper layer of aggregate (10–12in/25–30cm) may be an acceptable solution.

Selection of the Aggregate

There is a wide choice of material for the aggregate; the prime condition is that it should be an inert yet porous material. Well-weathered ash, granite, chips, coarse-quality sand or gravel, or pebbles can be used. Ashes, however, frequently render up sulphur fumes which could be very damaging to the tomato plants, and if used should be left outside in reasonably shallow layers for some time to leach thoroughly. Needless to say, there should be no contamination such as weedkiller in the aggregate chosen.

The aggregate should be put down in an even layer over the whole growing area; to leave patches of soil uncovered is to court trouble. It is, in fact, advisable to put the aggregate down over the whole floor area, and in areas not being used for cultivation to lay concrete slabs on top of the aggregate to form a path.

Selection, Filling and Placement of Rings

The selection of a container for the growing medium is not a vital matter. The most usual choice is a 9in (23cm) whalehide (bituminised paper) pot, usually without a base. Alternatively, 9–10in (23–25cm) clay pots with the drainage holes enlarged are frequently used, or rings may be made up of roofing felt or other suitable material, even linoleum. The 'rings' need not be round: boxes 10 x 10 x 10in (25 x 25 x 25cm) can be made up specially and serve very well. The only proviso is that contaminated material must not be used.

The rings are spaced out at the decided distance apart, which will generally be in the order of 20–24in (50–60cm). They can then be filled to within 2in (5cm) of the top with the appropriate compost, which is usually John Innes No 2. The recommendation that John Innes No 3 be used is frequently made, but the salt content of this is often far too high for young tomato plants and may cause root damage, apart from inhibiting growth. Soil-less media can also be used for ring culture, but liquid feeding must then be carried out from an early date.

Where rings or containers have bases, it is not necessary to fill them in position. It is frequently economically sensible to grow the plants in a warm propagating greenhouse for a period before setting them out in the growing greenhouse.

The quantities of compost required will vary according to the size of container selected, but if 9in (23cm) whalehide rings are used, approximately 12lb (5kg) of John Innes compost will be required to fill them to within 2in (5cm) of the top.

Note that the growing medium both in the rings and the aggregate should be sufficiently warm (56°F/13°C) to receive the plants when they are set out.

Summary of Preparations for Ring Culture

1 Remove border soil and make adequate provision for 'isolation' from any diseased soil.
2 Install inert aggregate 6–8in (15–20cm) deep (deeper with doubtful subsoil) and set out rings on top of this, filling either *in situ* or elsewhere.
3 Allow suitable time for both the growing medium in the rings and the aggregate to warm up (to 56°F, 13°C) before planting.

Special Aspects of Ring Culture

In the culture of tomatoes in borders, the plant has an uninhibited root run from the outset. In ring culture (and in some other systems) the roots are somewhat restricted in their early growth and this tends to act as a brake on over-development of stem and leaf. The vital difference between ring culture and other methods of culture involving limited quantities of growing media is that while some systems contain the roots in the medium throughout the season, with ring culture strong roots run into the aggregate, this usually coinciding with the period when the first truss of fruit has set and the swelling fruit acts as a natural brake on rank vegetative development. The root system which forms in the aggregate can in time take over the full growing function, but this transition must be allowed to take place naturally.

GROWING IN LIMITED QUANTITIES OF MEDIA

There are a considerable number of methods under this system and each is best dealt with individually, highlighting similarities with other methods. As referred to earlier, there has been very considerable adaptation of growbags and bolsters simply because of their convenience. They are simplicity them-selves to lay out in the greenhouse on a layer of polythene, although many gardeners now prefer to make a trench and line this with polythene so that when the growbags are slit on their undersides, the trench acts as a reservoir for moisture.

Bag Culture

This involves the use of approximately 12in (30cm) diameter plastic bags, with drainage holes. The size of these bags is not critical and they can be used for peat/sand, vermiculite, peat/perlite systems and other associated methods where free drainage is allowed by the porous open nature of the growing medium. Black polythene bags with drainage holes in their base, similar to those used for growing shrubs and trees in garden centres will also suffice and, as mentioned earlier, they should be 10–12in (25–30cm) in diameter when filled with the selected compost. Plastic buckets with holes bored out in them will also suffice. More recently however, especially in Scotland, there has been very considerable interest in larger bags containing $1\frac{1}{2}$ bushels (60 litres) of perlite, these being suitable for six plants.

The bags are contained in a polythene trough set up as shown in Fig 53 with a dam. Note that this system involves a reservoir system and it has been shown to produce very high yields, which is why it has been adapted by commercial growers. It is essential to appreciate that very strict control of nutrient levels is involved, which puts the system at this stage of development beyond the scope of the average amateur gardener, although the more meticulous tomato grower may well wish to take the system up. (*See* Appendix 4 for the address for details on this system).

The bags can be spaced out after filling at normal planting distances, or filled in position. It is normal to place them on a layer of polythene or, if adapting perlite systems, as previously described. There are many adaptations of this system, such as setting out on a layer of free-draining material such as inert gravel or even coarse sand. The use of perlite- or rockwool-filled bolsters is broadly similar to this system. Drainage can be a tricky matter and may involve slits in the side of the bag, but it cannot be emphasised too strongly the need for strict nutrient control with all these systems involving a limited amount of growing media. Watering and feeding systems are critical to be fully effective.

Growing in Boxes or Containers of Soil

This is a method favoured for smaller-scale growing by amateurs, whereby boxes or containers of a suitable size are filled with the selected growing medium, generally soil based, along with well-rotted FYM. Boxes or containers should preferably be at least 12–14in (30–35cm) in depth and of similar width and have drainage facilities in their base. These if wood should be treated with spirit-based preservative but definitely not with creosote, and the for free drainage is usually achieved by elevating the boxes on bricks. Apple or orange boxes are frequently used on a short-term basis, and these serve admirably.

Trough Culture, Peat-mattress Culture etc

There was, for a period, a vogue of using either elevated troughs or low-level trenches containing peat-based composts. With the peat-mattress system, whalehide pots containing either soil-based or soil-less media were placed on top of a layer of polythene which was then mulched with peat. Most of these systems tend to have been ousted or replaced by the use of bolsters or growbags. The basic philosophy behind these systems is similar.

Hydroponic Systems

There has inevitably been hybridisation or merging of hydroponic systems – where plants are grown in inert aggregates, usually inorganic. The perlite system discussed earlier is one of these, and there has also been previous reference to rockwool systems of culture. These systems depend on blocks of rockwool or perlite isolated from each other to avoid the spread of pests and diseases, it being noted that all water and liquid nutrients are best supplied by a spaghetti drip system on a strictly controlled basis. Nutrient film technique involves plants being grown in polythene troughs. It cannot be emphasised too strongly the need to obtain specialist help from the suppliers of equipment on setting up these systems and growing crops successfully. On a smaller scale, hydroponic tanks are available and I have personal experience in using these in a small greenhouse and, while full of trepidation at the outset, must admit that the results obtained were highly satisfactory, with few nutritional hiccups. (*See* Appendix 3 for details of NFT and Appendix 4 for addresses for further information on these systems.)

Growing in Whalehide Pots on Top of Soil

Where short-season crops only are concerned, plants can be grown with reasonable success in 9in (23cm) whalehide pots with bases, filled with growing medium, and placed on top of the greenhouse border. While any pests and diseases in the border may in time affect the plants, with a short-term crop this is not usually of great consequence. This is not a method, however, which can be recommended with any great degree of confidence, and it would be better to lay down polythene and set the plants on this, mulching with peat, which will result in a modified peat-mattress culture system (*see above*). Dwarf types can also be grown as pot plants.

STRAW-BALE CULTURE

Where the use of border soil is impracticable due to deep-seated virus infection of eelworm infestation and other methods are not acceptable, straw-bale culture is worth considering, especially by organic gardeners. There are tremendous advantages in using straw bales, not least of which is the heat generated by the decomposing straw and the CO_2 enrichment. It is also possible to have a quick turn-round from one crop, such as lettuce, to tomatoes, without recourse to sterilisation (growing in growbags, containers or trenches of course also allows this).

The harder-textured bales of wheat straw are preferable, as they retain shape better, failing which either oat or barley straw will suffice. It is better if the bales are wire-bound as string rots, permitting early collapse. While ideally the straw should be fresh, it matters little if it is slightly weathered, but bales stacked outdoors preparatory to use should be protected by polythene. The weight of bales varies, the average being 50–60lb (20–25kg). Straw treated with TBA or Picloram is unsuitable. With the development of 'jumbo' bales, a major problem could be obtaining small bales.

Wads or trenches of straw 7–10in (18–25cm) thick/deep can be used in preference to whole bales, and this method is of special interest in amateur growing where height is frequently restricted and there is difficulty in obtaining small bales.

'Composting' the Straw

Bales or wads of straw are placed in the most suitable position, taking into account the size of the greenhouse involved. Commercially either single or double lines of bales, end to end, are placed in rows 5ft (1.5m) apart, but this is frequently unsuitable in smaller greenhouses. My own greenhouse is 15ft (4.5m) wide and I find that two single lines of bales on each side and a double line in the centre is a convenient method of growing. This may allow fewer plants in the greenhouse (compared with other methods), but to compensate for fewer rows the plants are spaced closer, on average three per bale (or one per wad). The bales or wads are placed on layers of polythene (old polythene sacks are useful) to prevent contamination from greenhouse borders. Bales are laid flat to avoid toppling and it helps to conserve both space and water if they can be placed in a shallow $1^1/_2$–2in (3–5cm) depression. Take care to keep the wire binding-joints upwards to avoid puncturing the polythene. (Wire is seldom used now.)

About three weeks before the planting date, sufficient water is applied to thoroughly soak the bales, it being found that this is better carried out on several occasions over the space of a few days, and about 10gal (50 litres) of water per bale will be required – and pro rata for wads. The vents in the greenhouse are now closed and, if the weather is cold, the heating system is put into operation to provide about 50°F (10°C).

Fermentation Process

Considerable modification in treatment has taken place in recent years, the main difference being that smaller quantities of fertiliser and a shorter period are required for the fermentation process.

The basic objective is to get the bales to ferment and this requires the application on repeated occasions of quick-acting sources of nitrogen such as nitro-chalk. Quantities to apply vary but in general apply around $^3/_4$lb (336g) of nitro-chalk per average-sized bale and flush this in very thoroughly with water. It is stressed that less nitro-chalk can be applied, especially if worried about using this quantity of a fairly caustic fertiliser. In another three to seven days apply another dressing of nitro-chalk which should result in the bales starting to heat up. You can check this by pushing your hand into the bale. Finally, give a further light dressing of nitro-chalk and a complete base fertiliser containing trace elements, such as Vitax Q4. I do emphasise once again that the quantities of fertiliser are not critical and that the only objective is to get the bales heating, which may require more nitro-chalk than stated or less, according to the state of the straw and the prevailing temperature in the greenhouse. Considerable quantities of water are required to flush in the fertiliser, and this is best achieved by spraylines.

Organic gardeners will not be using inorganic fertilisers and will be turning to organic liquid fertilisers such as Maxicrop tomato special or similar. Here again it is difficult to state with any degree of exactitude the amount of Maxicrop to apply to get the bales heating satisfactorily, this being a question of trial and error.

Chempak offers a special straw-bale pack; use according to directions.

A small ridge of a mixture made up of 3 parts peat and 1 part sand is then run along the bales or wads after the final application of nutrients. This ridge merely needs to be large enough to accommodate the plant's rootball. A temperature check should be made on the bales and it will be found that the centres will reach 110–130°F (43–54°C). When the temperature falls to around 100°F (38°C) planting can take place.

Planting Procedure

Plants are set out at 12–14in (30–35cm) intervals (three per bale) and angled outwards, if practicable, so that they can be trained V-fashion. Wires can be used for support as the bales rot and drop, but if string is used this should be tied very loosely. The further implications of straw-bale culture are discussed in Chapter 10.

DOUBLE CROPPING

There is limited commercial interest in the technique of double cropping, when a **very early crop** is interplanted with another crop in June or July, the first crop eventually being removed to allow development of the later crop. Evaluation of double cropping compared to long-term single cropping must be a matter for individual decision according to the circumstances but with long season cropping now in vogue, it is only of limited interest. It is unlikely that smaller-scale growers or amateur gardeners will have much interest in double cropping, as they do not plant early enough to take a full crop off the first crop before it is removed to allow the second crop to develop. For convenience growbags or bolsters are generally used, and the full number required are spaced out at the beginning of the season, half being planted for the early crop and half for the later crop, on various permutations of spacing. Double cropping could operate with other cultural systems but less conveniently than with bolsters or growbags.

8
Planting

Cultural procedure follows a remarkably similar pattern no matter what method of culture is adopted and here I propose to deal with cultural techniques on a broad basis, making suitable comment on differing methods at the appropriate point. Details of modifications follow at the end of the chapter.

Planting Distances

The optimum number of plants per given area is a matter of considerable controversy. Some authorities recommend very close planting, whereas others maintain that yields per plant are greater when crops are less dense and each plant receives a better quota of light. Three factors must be considered when discussing planting distances: (1) the district, as I feel certain that areas of better light are more suitable for dense planting; (2) the variety, because healthy vigorous varieties take up more room than less vigorous ones; (3) the type of greenhouse and its orientation, a factor that does not affect density but has a considerable influence on placement. Where the greenhouse is east–west orientated a too-close longitudinal planting along the south-facing side will successively shade each row of plants and it is therefore better to have the plants more widely spaced longitudinally and closer on the east–west axis. Conversely north–south orientated houses are better planted more closely on the north–south axis and less closely on the east–west. The object in both cases is to allow better entry of solar radiation, the main source of which is of course from a southerly direction in the northern hemisphere.

Variation in plant densities is generally practised commercially rather than in amateur circles, yet, with the better all-round light admittance of the smaller amateur greenhouse the reverse could well be the case if it were not for the tremendous wastage of space occasioned by paths in proportion to total area. To appreciate this, think in terms of the total area of a greenhouse 8ft (2.4m) wide by 12ft (3.6m) long, which is 96sq ft (9m²). A path is necessary down the length of the greenhouse, and this is often as much as 3ft (90cm) wide: 3 x 12ft = 36sq ft (90cm x 3.6m = 3.24m²), which is over one-third of the total ground area. In commercial units it is usual to have path areas only about one-quarter to one-fifth of the total ground area (ie, leaving 75–80 per cent for cropping) and double rows of plants 15–24in (40–60cm) apart from each way sideways, the rows being spaced from 5–6ft (1.5–1.8m) apart centre to centre.

Planting densities on smaller greenhouses tend to be extremely variable, according to space available. Commercial plant densities have gone down in recent years, to anything between 9,000 and 11,000 plants per acre which

is around 4–5sq ft (1.2–1.5m²) per plant. A good average density in the
smaller amateur structure would be around 2 x 2ft (60 x 60cm) per plant
or some variation of this, with the plants closer in the rows, and with a
wider row spacing.

Planting distances are however not absolutely vital and it matters little
whether the plants are a few inches closer one way or another, although
excessively dense planting can bring problems of management and encourage
disease by restricting air movement. 'Compact' types of tomatoes can certainly
be grown more closely than vigorous types.

Spacing Modifications according to Cultural Methods

On straw bales, as we have seen, there must obviously be a closer planting
distance in the rows, congestion being overcome by modification of the training
system. Where other systems, including bolsters, are involved it will invariably be necessary to space the plants more closely in the rows, irrespective
of greenhouse orientation, although it is sometimes possible to plant across
the greenhouse. Commercially, spacings are on a 5–6ft (1.5–2m) double row
module (see Fig 28).

Soil Warmth and Plant Spacing

An issue of some importance with regard to plant spacing is the need to
ensure that plants are set out in a warm soil or growing medium – not less
than 56–57°F (14°C) at 5–6in (12.5–15cm) depth. Where a heating system is
specifically designed to give warmth in the immediate vicinity of plants this
temperature can be reasonably easily achieved, whereas with perimeter or
free-discharge, warm-air systems it may take a considerable time for suitable
temperatures to be reached. The need to avoid groth checks in young plants,
newly set out, cannot be over emphasised, as this will invariably result in early
infection from parasitic diseases, with serious long-term consequences such as
wilting or death. It is for this reason that small-bore pipe systems have become
so popular in commercial spheres, as they allow the heat to be taken to the
plants. On the Continent much use is made of underground alkathene pipes
appropriately installed to give the necessary soil warmth without the need to
'force' the heating system. Electric soil-warming cables, however, are much
more practical on a smaller scale.

Systems of warming rockwool and perlite bags can involve the use of polystyrene blocks indented to allow warm-water-filled PVC pipes, as shown in Fig 53.

Soil warmth does not cancel out the need for suitable air temperatures,
and this can only be accomplished with a well-designed heating system (see
Chapter 2).

WHEN TO PLANT

Recourse to the timetable in Chapter 5 will give information on the normal
programming for the crop. But there must be a critical appraisal of the actual,

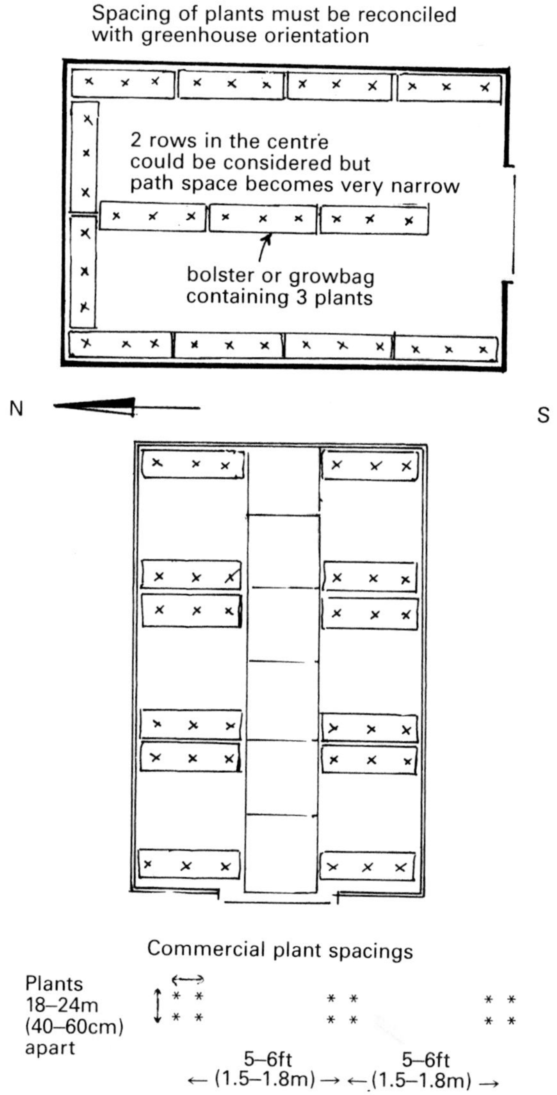

Spacing of plants must be reconciled
with greenhouse orientation

2 rows in the centre
could be considered but
path space becomes very narrow

bolster or growbag
containing 3 plants

N ← S

Commercial plant spacings

Plants
18–24m
(40–60cm)
apart

5–6ft
← (1.5–1.8m) →

5–6ft
← (1.5–1.8m) →

Fig 28 The spacing of growbags or bolsters in a 6 x 8ft (2 x 2.5m) greenhouse

compared to the theoretical temperature and light levels in the greenhouse in question. I am frequently asked to advise on the production of early tomatoes when reference to some literature has elicited the fact that tomatoes are planted in late January and early February in favoured climatic areas of good light. But to follow such procedure in a badly designed greenhouse in a poor light area would be folly, even if the necessary temperature levels could be readily enough achieved.

There is much virtue in paying heed to local trends. Obviously if there are a number of tomato growers in the area able to plant in late January or early February and obtain ripe fruit in late March or early April, then there are grounds for thinking that such practice can fairly readily be emulated. Some districts fall into the category of 'late' areas because of poor light occasioned by latitude, industrial pollution or sun shut-off by hills, and it would be very difficult to try and grow a really early crop of tomatoes under these conditions without recourse to artificial light. Good light intensities are essential not only to maintain photosynthesis at an acceptable level, but to encourage the formation of viable pollen. As the days get longer and lighter it is obviously easier to achieve this. A sensible appreciation of both natural light levels and the level of heating possible in the greenhouse and, more important still perhaps, the design of the heating system, should allow a planting time to be decided with fair accuracy. Mid-January to mid-March is most usual commercially, mid-March to mid-April for amateurs, and May for cold-grown crops.

At all events, and at the risk of repetition, it is essential to pre-warm either borders or the medium in which the plants are to be grown, and this could take ten to fourteen days or more, especially early in the year where the heating system is merely of perimeter design, or a lot less where there are soil-warming facilities. Unheated crops should not be planted until suitable soil temperatures have been achieved by warmth from the sun and there has been a general rise in the temperature night and day out of doors, and this can vary greatly according to district.

Greenhouse Temperature Levels

Reference to the table on page 85 gives the desired temperature levels for each stage of growth. It is unlikely that precise temperature levels of the order quoted will be constantly achieved by amateur gardeners, and in general terms around 60°F (16°C) day and night is a reasonable target, especially for northern growers. Solar radiation generally raises the daytime temperatures, whereas at night the temperature usually drops. However, there are some critical aspects of temperature control which are worth commenting upon.

Extremely high daytime temperatures lower fruit quality, especially as ripening commences. This is thought to be due to the drawing of moisture from the fruit to cope with the excessive temperature and the dry atmosphere frequently associated with it. On the other hand, warm air is able to 'hold' more moisture in gaseous form than colder air, and where an especially warm day is followed by a cold night, the gaseous moisture condenses on the cold glass and on the plants, causing an excessive rise in humidity. Obviously, therefore, there is considerable virtue in giving sufficient heat at night to avoid too much condensation and its attendant high humidity. Extremes are difficult to cope with in physiological terms. Plants, like animals, adapt themselves to a particular environment and tempo of growth. Alter this suddenly and adjustments must take place, but some form of debility also occurs. More will be said about this in Chapter 11.

The Planting Stage

Ideally, plants set out from mid-January to early March should have the first truss of flowers fully developed and one or two of the flowers fully opened.

If setting occurs on this truss soon after planting, this acts as an excellent 'brake' on rank vegetative development. For later planting it is also desirable, but not so essential, that the first truss should be showing as, with better light, growth is usually more restrained and balanced. Nevertheless there is still virtue in this flowering procedure, especially when soil has been steam sterilised and there is likely to be a flush of nitrogen. Apart from the restriction in vegetative vigour occasioned by a swelling first truss, there would appear to be no physiological reason why plants should not be capable of survival and good development if planted at various stages, although ideally a sturdy plant which stands about 9–12in (23–30cm) high (excluding pot) is desirable (usually higher for early-raised plants).

PLANTING PROCEDURE IN BORDERS

Marking out or planning preparatory to planting should be done with some precision, using either a steel tape or a measuring board. A garden line can then be used to keep plants in line, the actual placement of the plants being marked either with a cane or, less accurately, by indenting the soil. A frequent practice is to paint the heating pipes with white marks at the appropriate points. Alternatively plants can be placed on the soil at their approximate positions, then take out holes, accurately spaced, and leave these open for a few days before actually planting. This allows the soil to dry out a little if too wet, and at the same time the soil in the sides and base of the hole is warmed by solar radiation and air currents. This is important as these are the areas which will be first to contact the roots of the tomato plant.

Planting holes will vary in size according to the size of pot or block and can be taken out either with a trowel or a planting tool. Planting depth should be such that the seed leaves are an inch (2cm) or so above the soil level. Plants are watered before planting, and where plastic or clay pots have been used the rootball is carefully knocked out of the pot by tapping upside down on

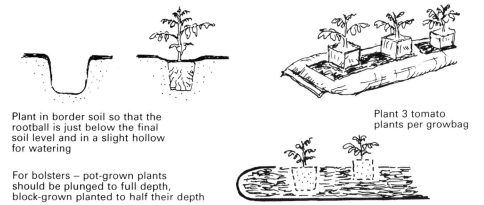

Plant in border soil so that the rootball is just below the final soil level and in a slight hollow for watering

For bolsters – pot-grown plants should be plunged to full depth, block-grown planted to half their depth

Plant 3 tomato plants per growbag

Fig 29 Planting tomatoes

a convenient hard surface. Paper or peat pots are better not removed, and blocks are of course planted intact.

Note that actual planting should not commence until the soil temperature at 4–6in (10–15cm) is 56–7°F (14°C) as registered on a soil thermometer.

Where plants are grown on in heated quarters before being set out, they are merely spaced out (if whalehide pots or other containers are used these must of course have bottoms to allow you to move the plants). Deep planting, on the other hand, can have its merits provided the soil is warm, and especially when, due to delays, plants have become very leggy. Layering can in this case be practised, setting the plant on its side and running the plant stem along a trench removed with a trowel, the object of this being to keep the bottom truss at a reasonable level and at the same time to encourage adventitious rooting along the stem length. After setting the plants in position they are firmed up with reasonable pressure.

Points to Note at Planting

1 Soil at planting time should be neither too wet nor too dry, but merely moist.
2 If soil is too wet planting should be delayed and the heating kept in full operation to dry it out.
3 If the soil is too dry apply a light overhead spray of water.
4 Soil should be neither too firm nor too loose, merely moderately compressed.

After planting, give plants a light watering in, about $^1/_4$ pint (140ml) per plant with plain water, or slightly more if the soil is very dry.

Planting Summary for Borders

Planting distance This is related in part to district, is closer in good light areas, wider apart in poor light areas. Plants are arranged, according to greenhouse orientation and cultural method, to avoid excessive shading to the south. Average planting allowance for small greenhouses is based on 2ft x 2ft (60cm x 60cm) square planting, or 14–18in (35–45cm) apart, in rows of $2^1/_2$–3ft (75–90cm) apart. Commercial growers tend to plant in double rows 5–6ft (1.5–1.8m) centre to centre – with plants spaced 16–24in (40–60cm) apart. Planting densities now average 8,000–12,000 plants per acre (20,000–30,000 per ha).

Planting time This is related to district, light and heat levels. On average it is from late January to early March in good light areas; March to April for mild heat; May for cold crops.

Soil temperature It is essential for it to be around 56–7°F (14°C) at 4–6in (10–15cm) depth, necessitating a well-designed heating system or a suitable 'wait' period – especially for unheated crops.

Temperature levels See page 85 for precise temperatures, but on average 60°F (16°C) day and night is reasonable in amateur greenhouses.

Planting This should be done with a trowel or planter; seed leaves should be 1in (2.5cm) or so above ground level, unless plants are very leggy, when they can be layered. Plants should be moderately firmed, unless planted on the surface.

Watering in Per plant give $1/4$ pint (140ml) or more if soil is dry.

MODIFICATIONS FOR DIFFERENT CULTURAL SYSTEMS

Planting procedure is basically similar whatever system of culture is practised.

Ring Culture and Similar Systems

Containers are placed in position, at the appropriate distance, filled with compost which is allowed to reach the requisite 56–7°F (14°C) before the plants are set out in the centre of the rings in the same way as for border culture, the plants being watered in similar fashion.

Straw Bales

The ridge of growing medium along the top of the bales or wads (*see* p 122) will usually achieve the necessary temperature without any difficulty. Plants are normally set out at three per bale, with the rootball covered, and well watered in. With wads, the same principle applies. Commercial spacings are as discussed for borders.

Containers and Troughs in general including Bolsters and Growbags

Spacings for all systems commercial are on the double-row system. Whatever type of container is involved, there is little need to vary planting procedure. The same is true of troughs. Care should be taken with soil-less, peat-based media to avoid saturation of the compost which inhibit roots by excluding air. The 'feel' of peat is the best guide to watering needs (squeeze a handful tightly to see if it retains its shape). Some peats dry out badly and are difficult to re-wet, leaving plants sitting high and dry.

With other systems, 'planting' procedures vary. Perlite bags involve putting the plants *on* the perlite; rockwool systems involve putting the rockwool block or cube on top of the rockwool slab. With hydroponic systems, whether NFT or tank systems, the plants are set out the appropriate distance apart, to give required plant densities. Usually one has guidance from the suppliers of equipment on this issue. This guidance is particularly important in systems where there is no 'buffering' or compensation, as happens when plants are grown in soil with its colloidal properties. This is no doubt the main reason why systems such as rockwool or perlite bags have not yet been launched on to the amateur market, the same being true of NFT trough systems as opposed to the tank system. As noted earlier, however, it is remarkable what range of salt concentrations and balance of nutrients tomato plants seem able to respond to. (*See* Appendix 3 for more detail on NFT and rockwool systems.)

9

Establishment and Training

EARLY TREATMENT OF PLANTS

Whatever system of culture is used, it is fundamental that the plants become established. This means that the roots should develop from the rootball, which exists in the pot or soil block, into the growing medium. The physiological processes involved in rooting are neither easy to understand nor to explain in detail. There must be a balance between the leaves and the root of the plant, and there is a close relationship between them. Allow the leaves to transpire to excess, as they will do in a hot, dry atmosphere, and this will slow up the formation of new roots. If the rootball is kept too dry this inhibits root development and simultaneously restricts leaf development. Other issues such as the salt concentration of the 'soil' water will also influence the rate at which roots develop and, should the salt concentration be too high, the growing point of the root will fail to extend, and this is also true of root hairs, the production of which, from existing roots, could be seriously affected. Excessively high salt concentrations in the medium can cause damage to roots by actual burning.

If the soil, compost, growing medium or nutrient temperature are too low, or the soil is too wet, roots may fail to develop, irrespective of all other considerations. Dieback of the roots can in fact take place, allowing the entry of parasitic fungi. It is perhaps difficult to understand why, in a sterilised (or, more accurately, pasteurised) growing medium, these parasites should exist in the first place, until it is appreciated that they are dispersed freely in the atmosphere and quickly invade all growing media, seeking a receptive host. Checked roots come into this category (*see also* Chapter 11) as there are weak cells to invade.

Conditions necessary for Establishment

Taking all these factors into account, it is a relatively straightforward matter to understand what conditions are necessary for ideal establishment. They can be summarised as follows:

1 High humidity of the atmosphere to reduce transpiration. This is achieved by restricting ventilation for several days and frequently damping down. Automatic ventilation systems or fans should therefore have their operating thermostats adjusted accordingly.
2 Warm soil or growing medium to encourage root development. Warm air to encourage leaves.
3 Just sufficient water to sustain growth with no wilting, and without over- watering, so excluding air. With nutrient film technique this is

overcome by intermittent flow, a matter which no doubt will be stressed by the suppliers of the equipment.

4 Salt solution of medium at the correct level so that plants are able to assimilate the right amount of water and nutrients. This can be ensured by accurate feeding, by making sure that liquid fertilisers are used at the correct dilution, and by avoiding excess of solid fertilisers (*see below*).

The basic philosophy underlying the various treatments suggested above is designed to encourage plants to develop a root system capable of sustaining the rapid vegetative growth made by foliage. Dry regimes or intermittent watering, as practised by some, endeavour, by limiting the amount of water available, to limit vegetative growth accordingly. It is a technique practised successfully by many, and unsuccessfully by many others. Obviously, however, if there is no restriction on the root development, vegetative growth often tends to be lanky and unproductive. Some dividing line must be drawn between the restriction of roots and enough early development to sustain growth, and it is here that containers come into their own, as the early root formation will be limited to the boundaries of the containers, and this in itself tends to have a braking effect on foliar development, and encourages the plant to produce flower trusses, which it may not do if growth is too rank.

It is usual to give only sufficient water to prevent wilting until it is seen by the freshening of the growing point that the plant has 'taken' and is starting to draw on the available nutrients in the soil. Different systems of watering will affect the rate of root development, and certainly a lot of watering will encourage surface and discourage basal rooting to the long-term detriment of the plant as the season progresses. Trickle irrigation systems tend to produce a cylindrical type of root, especially on light-draining soils. Soil-less media, especially if all peat, produce 'feather' roots, different in character to roots produced in soil. With hydroponic systems in general, growth is controlled by nutrient strength and balance.

Osmotic Feeding

It is at this stage that consideration can be given to the technique of osmotic feeding. To go back to soil preparation, it will be remembered that reference was made to the adjustment of soluble-salt levels to pC 2.8, so that there would be a measure of osmotic equilibrium, which in itself would tend to restrict growth even where quantities of nutrient and supplies of water in excess of the plants' needs are in reserve or given. To carry this a stage further, liquid feeds accurately diluted (pC 2.8 to 3) will help to sustain this osmotic equilibrium. The situation is still further enhanced if liquid feeds are balanced to the needs of the plant in respect of potash and nitrogen levels (*see* Chapter 3). (In general terms, high-potash feeds are usually required early in the year, particularly when a heat-sterilised, soil-containing medium is used – the same is true of hydroponic systems in their widest sense.)

'Weaning' the Plants

After the initial period of high humidity and establishment, the temperature should be kept at the appropriate level, and water given more freely according to weather patterns. Obviously the precision of temperature control will vary considerably, and where there are no automatic aids to ventilation and heating, it is a question of attempting to achieve as much regularity in temperature as possible. Marginal variations are not highly important, and indeed must be accepted in many instances. It would be difficult to state categorically that unless temperature levels are precise the crop will suffer in one way or another, as no one grower or research worker can state the ideal temperature pattern for any particular area, although she or he may have established that good results will invariably follow if certain recommendations are reasonably adhered to. It is the case, however, that where massive temperature variations do occur, as will certainly be the case in a completely unheated greenhouse, there can be undesirable side effects of which disease is obviously one. There will, as stated earlier, be physiological problems when a plant is expected to cope with immense temperature variations, and these occur not only within the processes of respiration, transpiration and photosynthesis, but within all related processes, especially nutrient uptake and the utilisation at night of carbohydrate manufactured during the day. The effect of temperature variations may be short- or long-term, and more probably a combination of both, but it is fairly certain that the most vital function of all, which is the production of flowers followed by successful fertilisation, will suffer in some way.

Some Aspects of Water Application

The earlier waterings will, as we have seen, be more or less confined to direct application in the vicinity of the rootball. Confusion frequently exists concerning the so-called searching of plants for moisture. Plants may not be capable of logical thought (although some research scientists think otherwise!) but they do respond to certain influences. The rate at which plants extend their roots from the rootball into the border or growing medium and subsequently develop them, is governed largely by the quantities of water and nutrient present where the plant roots are actually growing, and not merely because they seek it out. Perhaps there is rather a thin line of demarcation between the two principles, but in practical terms roots will actually develop better in areas of adequate moisture and nutrient (see table overleaf).

Supporting and Training

Tomato plants in their natural habitat, will sprawl about on the ground and have a bushy many-branched habit of growth. Cultural systems demand a rigid system of control involving support, shoot removal, and eventually a form of pruning or leaf removal. The exceptions are dwarf varieties grown in pots (eg 'Totem'), which form neat and compact little plants which need the minimum of support and training.

Establishment-period Watering Procedures for Different Cultural Systems			
Cultural system	First waterings of plants	Moisture state of growing medium	Humidity of atmosphere
Border, including grafted plants	Minimal watering in area of rootball	Keep just moist by damping	Frequent damping with fine rose overhead, especially mid-morning
Ring	Adequate watering of rootball frequently	Light waterings to be given in addition	Very frequent damping necessary due to the dry atmosphere which usually prevails
Straw bale	The whole of the growing-medium ridge is usually kept moist when bales are watered	Keep bales wet by use of hose or overhead sprays	Wetting the bales, usually helps to keep the atmosphere sufficiently moist, but damp down also if necessary
Polythene bag, bolster, trough and trench culture	Only minimal watering required in area of rootball	Peat-based media usually retain their moisture content well, provided they are sufficiently damp at planting time	Damp down as for border culture
Peat mattress	A compromise between ring – and bag – culture treatments. Light rootball waterings only	As above, but ensuring that the small amount of growing medium in ring does not dry out	If peat mattress is moist this usually ensures a sufficiently high humidity but damp down on bright days
Container systems	Where soil-based medium is used, treat as for border culture. For soil-less medium exercise the same care as for bags (see above)	Large bulks of growing medium will usually require no further watering, apart from damping, until plants are established	Frequent damping down, especially for raised-box systems.
Hydroponic systems in general which includes perlite bags, rockwool and NFT	It is a question of strict monitoring of water in early stages and deciding whether to have a continuous flow with NFT or intermittent watering		Frequent damping down

Note The subject of watering and nutrition, both early and late in the season, is dealt with in detail in the next chapter.

Support

Plants require support from an early stage, and while I am unaware of any experimental work concerned with the actual effect of early or late support, the fact remains that once plants are supported they appear to grow faster. Plants should be supported within a day or two of planting, although it does not appear to do much harm if support is delayed until the odd plant topples, which it will tend to do when heavy damping down has taken place. There are various ways of supporting plants: a popular method in amateur circles is to tie the plants to tall canes, but this system obviously has many drawbacks, especially on hygienic grounds. While methods of supporting plants can vary considerably, the use of strained horizontal wires at a height of around 6–12ft (1.8–3.6m) from the ground is basic, and the position of these should coincide with the rows of plants unless the V-training system employed in straw-bale culture is adopted, when wires must be positioned, after measurement, from a point 12–20in (30–50cm) from the ground level, to overhead wires in both directions.

For support, a 3- or 5- ply soft twine or Italian hemp is used, although recently polypropylene twine has become very popular, as it is extremely durable. It is highly important that any wire used overhead must be of sufficiently thick gauge and secured firmly to the greenhouse or structure, as a laden crop of tomatoes can be very heavy. Some modification to the greenhouse or structure is often necessary for this. The soft twine or string should be tied in a loose loop with a non-slip knot above the cotyledon (seed leaves) but below the lower leaves (*see* Fig 30).

Plant hook wires $^3/_{16}$in (5mm) thick and 18in (45cm) long are advisable for straw bales and lateral training systems generally, in the first case to avoid strain on the plant roots from the decomposing bales, and in the latter case to keep the first truss of fruit from trailing on the growing medium. Alternatively a horizontal wire can be run along, about 12in (30cm) above the growing

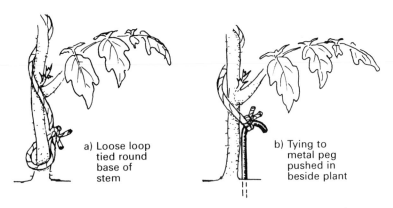

a) Loose loop tied round base of stem

b) Tying to metal peg pushed in beside plant

Fig 30 Two methods of tying the string at the base of the tomato plant

17 To be commercially productive there must be consistent work on training systems to give the maximum number of trusses

medium, supported by stout wooden pegs, and this is often more practical for oblique and layering systems.

Plant Training

Plants are usually, but not necessarily, twisted clockwise round the string, taking care not to snap off the growing point, something which can easily happen when plants are turgid (full of moisture) or growth is very hard. There are several methods of training plants, best explained diagramatically. With modern vigorous varieties, especially when planting fairly early with adequate heat, it will be necessary to evolve some system of training other than simply growing the plants vertically and pinching out the growing points as has been the practice for many years.

Fig 31 Tomato training   Twist plant clockwise   Take string under the trusses

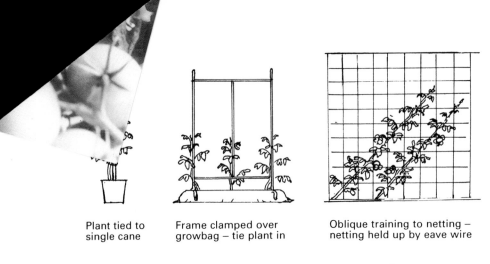

Plant tied to
single cane

Frame clamped over
growbag – tie plant in

Oblique training to netting –
netting held up by eave wire

Fig 32 Training systems suitable for the small greenhouse

Vertical training The plants are allowed to reach the horizontal wires before being stopped. This system is frequently used in amateur circles on any system of short-term culture. Where it is carried out on longer-term crops, the plants can be arched over the wires. In commercial circles, a modified Guernsey arch system can be adopted with the head of the plant allowed to dip before being taken up vertically again. A modification of this is the Dutch hook system where the plants are taken along rather than across the rows, the stems being contained in plant hooks on the top wires. Both of these systems are highly labour intensive.

V-training This system, where the plants are trained out obliquely and alternately in different directions, is useful with straw bales as the plants are set so closely together, although vertical or other training can also be carried out. It makes arching a little more difficult to achieve.

S-hook system This system is popular and involves the use of 16 gauge S-hooks set appropriately, the plants being supported so many hooks along and dropped a hook as the season progresses, so that the plants are progressively layered. Wires or plant hooks are desirable to avoid the bottom truss trailing on the growing medium. At the ends of the rows the plants are turned on to the next row. With smaller amateur greenhouses this system can be very difficult to achieve, especially when there may only be one row of plants to begin with. With this system considerable defoliation is necessary.

Layering Here the plants are initially trained vertically, being completely detached when they reach the horizontal wire, and layered – usually at the stage where lower trusses are picked and where the ripening trusses are kept well above growing-medium level. I have experimented with this system in my own greenhouse, and it can be achieved with a little planning, even if space is restricted. Once again, regular defoliation is necessary to allow this system to be achieved. Spare twine is contained on special 'coathangers'.

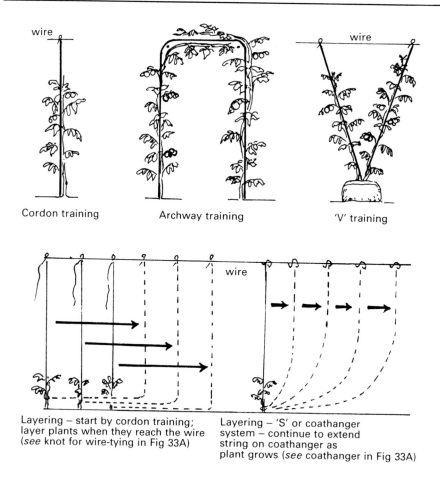

Cordon training   Archway training   'V' training

Layering – start by cordon training; layer plants when they reach the wire (*see* knot for wire-tying in Fig 33A)

Layering – 'S' or coathanger system – continue to extend string on coathanger as plant grows (*see* coathanger in Fig 33A)

Fig 33 Systems of training used by professional growers

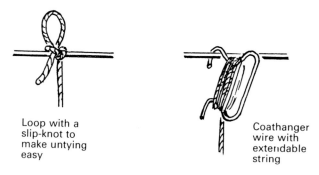

Loop with a slip-knot to make untying easy

Coathanger wire with extendable string

Fig 33a Systems for attaching training string to the wire

Lateral training From the outset plants are trained obliquely at an angle of 35–46°, wide mesh or polypropylene netting being a useful supporting medium for accomplishing this without a great deal of string manipulation. The plants are tied on to the netting with small loops of string, wire or paper clips. It is usual to lower the plants as the season progresses. This is however easier if slip lateral strings are looped round vertical strings.

The Merits of the Different Training Systems

The choice of any particular training system will depend not only on the length of the growing season but also on the type of greenhouse and whether ventilation can be effectively carried out to overcome the problem of disease which occurs more readily in systems other than the vertical. Laterally trained plants from the outset appear to be most prone to disease attack, due to restriction of air movement, and plants layered later in the season eventually suffer a similar disadvantage. It is important to note the information below on defoliation. *In all systems it is desirable to have the top 3–4ft (1m) of growth vertical.*

18 Training tall plants can be made easier by using foot-stands

PLANT PRUNING
Side-shoot Removal

This must be carried out from the outset, restricting the plants to one main stem, unless under special circumstances such as filling up a gap left by a plant loss. Removal is best effected when the side shoots are young, and preferably when turgid (full of moisture). There is little problem in the whole process of side-shoot removal, the little shoots merely being snapped off with the finger and thumb. Some varieties tend to form two leading shoots and it is necessary to decide which one is to be removed. This is not a vital matter, although if only one shoot bears a flower truss, let this one remain. Suckers forming at ground level should be removed, this especially so with grafted plants. Some say that removing side shoots with the fingers rather than a knife avoids the spread of virus disease, but I find it difficult to accept this. Indeed the use of a knife dipped regularly in a mild sterilant could be more desirable than virus-infected fingers if barrier creams are not used.

When side shoots are allowed to get too large before removal, the scar left can readily become disease infected, especially later in the season; *side-shoot scars are a very susceptible entry point for botrytis spores.*

Removal of Lower Leaves

This should start when the leaves concerned have outlived their usefulness, this being indicated by their yellowing. Lower leaves can also serve as a source of fungus disease, particularly when the plant begins to hang with fruit and the lower leaves trail on the ground. It is usual merely to remove the foliage up to the ripening truss, and obviously one of the main benefits of leaf removal is that air is allowed to circulate through the base of the plants. Some growers remove leaves ruthlessly, leaving only 3ft (1m) of unleafed stem growing vertically. This level of pruning is necessary when layering systems are practised. Pruning of plant leaves has certain physiological effects on the

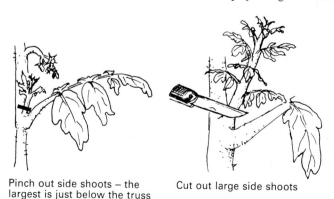

Pinch out side shoots – the largest is just below the truss

Cut out large side shoots

Fig 34 Removal of side shoots

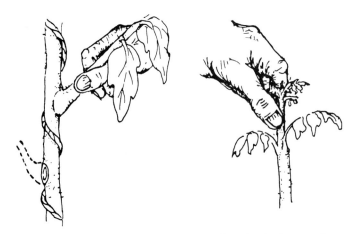

Fig 35 (left) Deleafing; Fig 36 (right) Stopping leader growth

plant, one of which is the hastening of ripening. If pruning is carried out to excess the fruit may be smaller and quality could suffer, although there are no hard and fast rules about this.

The best way to remove leaves is, in my opinion, with a quick up-and-down movement when the plants are well supplied with moisture – certainly not in the heat of the day when their moisture content is at its lowest, and when leaf removal might result in disease-prone tears or snags. Painting any rough snags with a fungicide is an excellent preventative against disease infection.

Stopping

Opinions differ on the virtue of restricting the heights of plants to a given level. Usually this is dictated by the height of the top wire, unless the plants are to be arched or layered (*see* Fig 33). Stopping the plants usually takes place when there is little hope that any further fruit trusses allowed to form will ripen before the plants have to be removed, either because the season is coming to a close or in the interests of another crop.

It appears that stopping does not restrict the upward flow, as any side shoots allowed to remain at the top of the plant develop very quickly. One reason for stopping is to avoid a clutter of leaves on the roof of the greenhouse and it could be said to be necessary on purely environmental rather than physiological grounds. Dutch research workers feel that it is better to allow the plants to continue growing and merely remove the flower truss.

In practice all that is required is to cut or snap off the top of the plant immediately above a leaf joint, avoiding the removal of any flower or young fruit truss which has a chance of ultimately producing ripe fruit. In amateur houses with low heat levels it is unlikely that trusses in flower after the middle of August will become fertilised and produce ripe fruits on the plant, although with good heat and light levels fertilisation can occur later – well into October – producing ripe fruit as late as Christmas, which is a special treat and makes tomato-growing well worthwhile!

10

General Growing Procedures

The so-called 'blueprint' growing which is the yardstick for commercial production would seem at first sight merely to consist of adhering exactly to a prescribed growing programme. Matters are, however, more complicated than this, and it is the intelligent manipulation of all the various factors which brings success. While the automatic aids which are becoming commonplace both in commercial and amateur circles, take much of the guesswork out of things, there are still a great many decisions to be made, not only on the whole growing programme, but on a day-to-day basis as occasioned by changing climatic patterns and plant response to environmental variations.

Main Factors Requiring Attention

A great difficulty for many amateur gardeners is their absence at business for five or six days a week, leaving the plants, even with certain automatic aids, to cope with further variables. This section deals with the most important issues and the ones which require constant attention.

Young tomato plants, as they become successfully established, start to show a freshening of the growing point, resulting in extension growth and the production of new leaves. Flower trusses are of course present in the plant before planting, although not always visible or in actual flower. The vegetative development of the plant, including flower-truss formation, subsequent setting and fertilisation, and swelling of fruit, is entirely dependent on light, temperature, water and nutrient supply, and the inter-reaction of these with each other. The concentration of CO_2 (carbon dioxide) in the atmosphere is also an important factor in development, owing to the effect this has on the speed of the photosynthetic process.

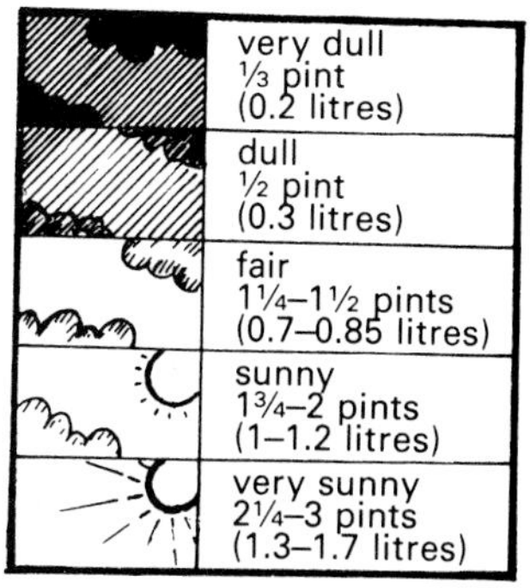

	very dull ⅓ pint (0.2 litres)
	dull ½ pint (0.3 litres)
	fair 1¼–1½ pints (0.7–0.85 litres)
	sunny 1¾–2 pints (1–1.2 litres)
	very sunny 2¼–3 pints (1.3–1.7 litres)

Fig 37 The water requirements of the tomato plant according to weather

Amount required per day
when plant is 3ft (1m) or more

Moisture Supplies

Water supplies should be controlled as carefully as the method of application allows. Plants supplied with an excess of water tend to go lighter in colour, and yellowing of the bottom leaves frequently occurs due to the exclusion of air from the growing medium and the reduction in nitrogen supply. Plants short of water, apart from drooping and wilting badly on hot days, tend to go darker green in colour, and leaves may also go hard and brittle as the plants cannot assimilate nutrients, not only because of the actual lack of water as a conveying medium, but also because of the raising of the salt content of the soil (*see below*). It is of some importance to consider water supplies in conjunction with nutrient supplies, as the two are virtually synonymous.

Nutrient Supplies

Providing the right amounts of Nitrogen, Phosphorus and Potassium			
Nutrient	*Excess*	*Deficiency*	*Comments*
Nitrogen	Lush, light-green, excessively curly, top leaves early in the season. Thin tops later in year, coupled with long internodes (distance between leaf joints). Trusses may partially form or alternatively be very profuse and gross on thick stems and subsequently fail to flower or set properly. In extreme cases this will persist throughout the season, resulting in very poor yields.	Poor, sickly looking plants with thin, hard stems, and general lack of vigour; yellowing of lower leaves may also ocur in severe cases.	It is important to maintain a balance between nitrogen and potash, as shortage of one can result in excess of the other and vice versa.
Phosphorus	Difficult to diagnose visually and does not readily give rise to problems, as surplus phosphorus tends to become unavailable.	General lack of phosphorus in soil will tend to result in unproductiveness and delayed flowering and fruiting. Temporary lack occasioned by coldness causes blue colouration of leaves.	An element which is not mobile which explains why symptoms of excess or shortage are not so clear as with nitrogen and potash. Apart from this the tomato plant's need for phosphorus is not great.
Potassium	Dark-coloured leaves but stems with very short internodes and curled leaves throughout the whole plant. Flower trusses very squat. A great excess of potash will produce scorching of leaf tips (*see also* 'Osmotic feeding' p 144).	Much the same symptoms as with excess of nitrogen, with marginal leaf scorch occurring in extreme cases.	The link between nitrogen and potash balance is a vital one for tomato plants.

Light Intensities

Poor light, as occasioned by district or weather pattern, will result in thin plants of a pale green colour, with long internodes (the distance between the leaf joints). The height of the first truss will also be affected and successful fertilisation can be difficult, especially if there is industrial contamination which stains the glass and further restricts light levels. Good light results in a sturdy, dark-green, short-jointed plant which should produce full, fertile flowers of good colour, capable of setting provided there is a correct nutrient balance. The difficulties of good fertilisation early in the season are largely the outcome of poor light, although there are certainly nutritional complications (*see below*). The practice of using hormone setting liquid is fairly widespread in difficult situations: it is essential that these setting hormones are used strictly according to directions and not to excess, otherwise distorted poor quality fruits may be produced.

Temperatures

Low temperatures day and night will generally slow up rate of growth. High daytime temperatures in good light followed by cool nights will result in a plant with curled leaves and short internodes and there can be gross truss formation (huge, extended trusses) and bad setting owing to the excess accumulation of carbohydrates. High night and low day temperatures will produce 'played out', thin plants with long internodes. The warmer the soil, or growing medium or nutrient solution, up to about 75°F (24°C), the greater the rate of root development. A temperature of around 65°F (18°C) is ideal, although a higher range of temperatures seems to suit rockwool, perlite and NFT systems, in the order of 77°F (25°C). Air temperatures should be adhered to as strictly as possible.

SEASONAL FEEDING PROGRAMME

Few tomato plants are planted into soils or growing-media of low nutrient content, and it has been explained in Chapter 7 why in fact such a procedure is not desirable (*see also below*). While the broad approach to nutrition can be made to sound relatively simple, it must be appreciated that there are considerable complications, which can arise in both soil and, more particularly, in soil-less media, rock wool and perlite or with NFT; with the best will in the world it is impossible to approach tomato nutrition in such a precise manner than an automatically foolproof system of feeding is possible. Conditions are bound to vary very considerably between soils or other substrates, and apart from this there are temperature and light patterns, water quantities and countless other variables. It must be appreciated, however, that visual appreciation of the progress made by the plant is essential, even if the grower has ready access to laboratories for seasonal checks and has automatic dilution apparatus.

Osmotic Feeding

For the process of osmosis to be effective there should be a difference between the respective osmotic pressures in the plant and the soil. Assuming that the plants are set out in soil or growing media of any type which is known to be of an acceptable salt level, the plants are developing their root systems in the midst of a compatible chemical environment. The vital issue is the strength of the solution of salts, as this determines the rate at which the plants assimilate their moisture and nutrients, which in effect means rate of growth. Translate this salt solution into more practical terms – the available amount of nitrogen and potassium and other salts – and one moves a step nearer the whole concept of nutrition. The rate of growth of a tomato plant in a warm greenhouse is tremendous, and vast demands are made on the store of nutrients. Unless one is able to keep the soluble-salt strength within the prescribed concentration and at the same time ensure that the requisite amounts of nitrogen and potash are there in correct ratio to each other, the whole system breaks down. Matters are not quite so bad as they sound, of course, as the micro-organisms in soil-based media will do much to keep the balance of nutrients stable, but this unfortunately is not the case with soil-less media or nutrient solutions.

Practical Approach to Nutrition

Assuming that there is a liberal supply of nutrients present in the first case, the next step is to estimate, both by visual means and by previous experience, whether the plant's diet is suitable. The following is the generally accepted nutritional pattern:

1 High potash feeds are required early in the season, especially in heat-sterilised soil, and with vigorous varieties on other systems.
2 Standard feeds are required during the major part of the season.
3 High-nitrogen feeds are required late in the year, when the reserves of nitrogen tend to be played out and the plants require a boost to encourage vegetative development.

It rests entirely with the grower or gardener, however, to assess the needs of her or his plants and to apply the necessary balance of feeds according to the symptoms exhibited by the plants, and there can obviously be no pre-set pattern in the face of all possible variables.

Proprietary Liquid Feeds

There are many proprietary feeds available and it is necessary to use these according to directions. Make sure that they have the correct dilutions and nitrogen to potash ratio. ICI, Chempak and Vitax offer an excellent range of liquid feeds of varying analysis, and there are many others in the market.

Liquid Feeds regularly used by Growers						
Dilution rate	K₂O to N ratio	Potassium nitrate	Urea*	or	Ammonium nitrate*	ppm (mg/litre) N K₂O
1–200	3–1 high potash	150g/litre 24oz/gal				105 335
1–200	2–1 standard	150g/litre 24oz/gal	31g/litre 5oz/gal	or	37g/litre 6oz/gal	170 335
1–300	1–1 high nitrogen	150g/litre 24oz/gal	100g/litre 16oz/gal	or	130g/litre 21oz/gal	225 225
1–200	1–1.5 medium/high nitrogen	150g/litre 24oz/gal			68g/litre 11oz/gal	225 335

* These are 'stock' solutions diluted 1–200 parts water: 1fl oz stock solution in 1.25gal water (5ml/litre).

Solid Feeding

Most proprietary fertilisers, straight fertilisers or self-formulated mixes can be used, for border-grown plants especially, adhering again to directions in the case of proprietary types, or the recommended rates for straight fertilisers. Most proprietary, solid-type fertilisers are used every 10–12 days at 1–2oz per sq yd (33–67g/m²).

Note that some solid fertilisers are particularly concentrated and that roots and stems may be damaged irreparably by excess or careless application. Solid fertilisers cannot be absorbed by the plant roots until they are dissolved, which means watering in or, alternatively, making sure that they are applied to a damp soil. Care should be taken to avoid 'swirling' of recently applied fertilisers, which may result in concentrated patches.

These remarks about solid feeding apply primarily to border cultivation. Solid feeds, however, can be used in straw-bale culture, box culture or other systems where there is enough space to flush in solid feeds. Generally speaking, however, when growing in limited quantities of growing medium, liquid feeding is much safer and more effective. Solid feeding has no real role in systems such as rockwool, perlite bags or NFT.

Constant versus Intermittent Feeding

What has already been said about the osmotic process will, I feel, do much to clarify precisely why it is desirable to have a constant and evenly diluted solution of fertilisers. Intermittent feeding with liquid or solid fertilisers will obviously result in a varying salt solution in the soil or growing medium, but not necessarily to a degree which will upset the plant greatly, although the first symptoms of shortage of salts will inevitably be blotchy ripening

19 Diluters for accurately measuring and 'dosing' are an essential part of modern tomato culture

of fruit (*see* p171). There is virtue, therefore, in never applying plain water for border cultivation, but according to the present state of knowledge it is doubtful whether constant feeding is desirable for systems involving limited amounts of growing media, especially if these are peat-based. Experience has shown that a rapid buildup to a toxic level can occur where constant liquid feeding is carried out in peat-based media, and this indicates the desirability of flushing out with plain water frequently when analysis proves this necessary.

There is a clear set of rules to follow for the accepted osmotic procedure and these are detailed on pages 144 and 145. It is important to get the balance of nitrogen to potash as exact as possible; the most important thing is to get the dilution of liquid feed right, and a guide to the right balance of nitrogen to potash is by observing growth, as far as this is practical. With soil-less media watch particularly for any symptoms of nutritional imbalance such as scorching or bleaching of growing points, along with 'black bottoms' on the base of fruit (*see* Chapter 11). Flush out with plain water when this occurs and start feeding again with the appropriate ratio of nitrogen/potash as indicated by the general development of the plant. Where improvement does not occur almost immediately, consult someone qualified to give expert assistance.

Summary of Feeding Programme

Liquid fertilisers Potash nitrate/urea or ammonium nitrate; 1–200 dilution. High potash early in season, standard when plants show steady growth, high nitrogen later in season.

Proprietary liquid feeds Use as directed, adhering rigidly to instructions.

Solid feeds – straight Apply at rates shown in table on pages 55–7, every 10–12 days, for border-grown or straw-bale plants.

Solid feeds – proprietary Apply at recommended rates every 10–12 days.

Practise constant liquid feeding early in season and continue with more restricted feeding later, provided no symptoms indicative of salt-concentration trouble develop. Look particularly for blotchy ripening of fruit (indicative of low salt concentrations in the soil, especially likely in soil-less media) or 'black bottoms' (indicative of high salt concentration) and flush with water in the latter case. Where complicated symptoms occur, seek specialist advice. Total water requirements should relate to the table on page 141. (*See* p170 for details of nutritional upsets.)

Foliar Feeding

There is great interest these days in foliar feeding, the plants absorbing the nutrients directly into their leaves, therefore by-passing the normal root uptake. This is particularly useful for applying magnesium and calcium (*see* p52–3) to avoid the 'shut-off' or unbalanced complications which generally cause these deficiencies in the first case. Osmotic principles, however, still apply, and excess concentration of foliar feeds will cause damage to the leaves.

A quick response is generally achieved by foliar feeds. Special foliar feeds are available, but most of the normal liquid fertilisers applied by overhead spraylines can serve admirably. Some growers allow the fertiliser some 20–30 minutes to be absorbed into the leaves and then flush off with plain water to avoid any damage which could be caused by the nutrients concentrating in localised areas of the leaves in hot sun. It is worth noting that surplus foliar feed which is not absorbed by the foliage and which runs off may be eventually taken up by the plant roots anyway. Some sceptics maintain that this is the main role of foliar feeds.

Mulching

This is mainly for border-grown plants, using organic materials. The practice of mulching is not carried out as widely as it was many years ago, when the application of well-rotted FYM to borders in May or June was routine practice. While peat can be used as a mulch, plastic floor-lining material is now universally used commercially for all systems of culture. There are several reasons for mulching:

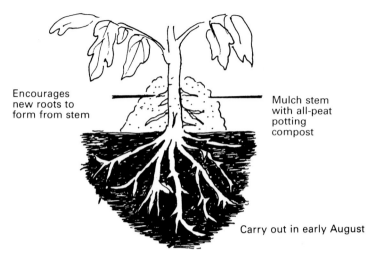

Encourages
new roots to
form from stem

Mulch stem
with all-peat
potting
compost

Carry out in early August

Fig 38 Mulching or 'necking-up' tomato stems (in border culture)

1 To avoid surface evaporation of moisture
2 To encourage the formation of surface adventitious roots (organic mulches)
3 To provide a ready source of nutrients in acceptable form to the surface-feeding roots (organic mulches such as FYM)
4 The use of floor liners improves light reflection, keeps the crop clean and of course controls weeds.

If FYM is used it should be very well rotted, otherwise damage can result from ammonia release. Peat is much more palatable to the plant if approximately 5–6oz (140–170g) per bushel (36 litres) of ground limestone is added. Fertiliser can also be added to the peat, although it is better to wait until roots are developed and apply fertilisers or liquid feeds on the basis of the normal feeding programme. Peat mulches are especially useful where there is some root or vascular-tissue damage due to a fungal agency or in the case of severe potato cyst eelworm attack (*see* pp163 and 169).

CULTURAL MODIFICATIONS FOR OTHER SYSTEMS
Ring Culture

It has already been explained that initially the roots are contained in a ring; at this stage the plants are watered and fed as described for border culture. It will be found that more water is required when the plants develop as the containers dry out rapidly, and I feel it would be inadvisable to apply constant liquid feeding in this instance, otherwise there could be a salt-concentration problem. The roots very soon grow into the aggregate, evidence of this being the mass of fine root hairs in the vicinity of the rings, and before long the root system in the aggregate can be extensive. Early in the season all the water needed should be applied to the rings, and the roots which form in the aggregate will be supplied by the surplus which drains out of the rings. It is unnecessary and inadvisable to apply extra water to the aggregate early in the season, other than that applied for damping-down (to raise the humidity for fertilisation purposes). All feeding is initially given through the rings.

As the season progresses water is given to the aggregate, while keeping the rings moist, and then water is progressively concentrated in the aggregate to encourage a gradual takeover of functions. The rings should gain all the moisture they require by capillary (upward-pulling) action. Take care, however, not to allow complete drying out of the rings until the season is well advanced. Feeding is applied to the aggregate when it is seen that the takeover is more or less complete, this generally occurring when the plants are about 5–6ft (1.5–1.8m) tall. Any wilting that takes place indicates that the plants are still depending on the rings. The root restriction early in the year is extremely conducive to fruit production, and when strong growth is needed thereafter, the roots in the aggregate are capable of sustaining growth throughout the season. Support, training and general cultural procedure is similar to that for border culture.

Grafted Plants

A slow start is typical of grafted plants, especially if root disturbance has occurred when the fruiting-variety root is removed at planting. Once plants do get under way, however, they develop great vigour and cultural procedure is similar to that described for border culture, especially with regard to removal of basal suckers.

Straw Bales

The need to maintain water supplies is the main problem with straw bales, and some 'automatic' watering system such as drip nozzles or perforated hose is desirable, coupled with draping the bales with polythene, leaving only a section of the soil ridge exposed. There can be 'locking up' of nitrogen early in the season due to the concentration of bacteria in the decomposing straw, thus necessitating the application of extra nitrogen; thereafter there can be a surplus of nitrogen, necessitating liberal potash additions, especially to keep fruit quality high.

Other Systems

Most of the problems are nutritional and have already been referred to. The physical application of water is a problem with some systems, unless drip or other methods of watering are adopted.

This applies especially to bolsters, perlite bags, rockwool or other container systems, liquid feeding being carried out on a precise and progressive basis, noting the need for trace elements, especially for rockwool or perlite-bag systems. It is not the intention of this book to deal in detail with these systems, as they tend to be highly specialised, and as has been stressed before, precise cultural advice is necessary, ideally from the suppliers of the equipment, who will also provide the necessary range of liquid feeds. Several companies provide the basic chemicals, also a complete liquid fertiliser containing trace elements.

Important Note

The frequency with which liquid fertiliser is applied with all systems involving limited quantities of growing media must be the subject of constant check if salt problems are to be avoided, especially where there is excessive moisture loss, as with ring culture, straw bales or polythene-bag culture. Reference back to the total quantities of nutrients required by plants as detailed in Chapter 4 is advisable, but constant visual assessment is still of prime importance.

From Fruit-picking Stage to End of Season

Picking tomato fruit is a relatively simple task, the main provision being that the fruit is removed by snapping the stem and preferably not by removing the fruit from the calyx. It is important to handle fruits carefully and keep them cool especially in hot weather. Leaving the fruit lying about in the greenhouse or even in the sun out of doors, is certain to induce softening. The stage at which to pick the fruit depends on whether it is to be consumed immediately or whether it is to be sold; it should be noted that where wholesale marketing is involved, compulsory grading standards apply (*see* Appendix 2), and details of these are available from any Ministry of Agriculture advisory officer. Fruit intended for wholesale markets is usually picked one or two days before full ripeness. Grading machinery is necessary for large-scale culture and fruit is marketed in standard fibreboard trays containing 6kg (13lb 4oz) of fruit.

Crop Finishing

Reference has been made earlier to the nutritional pattern necessary for sustaining growth, usually by varying the nitrogen to potash ratio, ranging from high potash early in the season to high nitrogen late in the season. It is important to keep a strict watch on the general vigour of the plants and apply the corrective treatment at the right time as the real success of the tomato crop depends on the overall performance, not merely on the early crop.

'Fade-out' of plants due to a variety of causes can frequently occur and these are detailed in Chapter 11. Maintaining a healthy vigorous root system right to the end of the season is not always easy in older borders which have

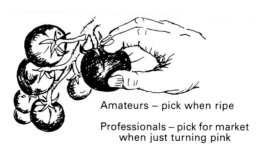

Amateurs – pick when ripe

Professionals – pick for market
when just turning pink

Fig39 Picking tomatoes

been in cultivation for many years. Despite sterilisation, root rots and vascular diseases can quickly reduce end-of-season vigour, as indeed can virus infection or eelworm infestation contracted from deeply seated sources. This is in fact the main reason why systems other than border culture are finding such favour.

End-of-season Watering Patterns

These can be confusing as, while a plant in full vigour will use the calculated or estimated amount of water (*see* p141), a heavily de-leafed plant, especially if suffering from root or stem disorders, is unlikely to assimilate large quantities of water. It must also be remembered that even in the case of a plant with a healthy root system some natural root death occurs. Nevertheless, as the season progresses the main roots can become fairly extensive and the plant is able to draw on the reserve of water in the soil at lower levels. This explains why, despite the cessation of regular watering which often accompanies the general lack of gardening enthusiasm at the end of the season, the plant continues to grow strongly. There is in fact some virtue in restricting water quantities at the tail-end of the season as it seems to encourage the ripening of remaining fruit.

A further point of importance is that the high humidity of the atmosphere which often occurs naturally out of doors in August/September/October gives rise to a humidity problem in the greenhouse which encourages disease. The excess application of water raises the humidity pattern still higher, and botrytis can become a major problem. The application of less water at this late stage in the season will help to keep humidity down and, coupled with this precaution, heat should always be given at night, to avoid temperature variations and condensation.

Removal of Plants

When it is decided to remove the plants, all the remaining fruit is picked and either ripened at a light window or on a greenhouse bench. Green fruit can of course also be used for making chutney. The plants are cut 9–12in (23–30cm) above ground level and detached from their strings, after which they are dumped some distance from the greenhouse. Alternatively they can be destroyed by burning as soon as dry enough. The plant stems are then gently forked out of the soil with as much root as possible, watering the border to facilitate this if necessary. The plant roots should also be disposed of away from the greenhouse, or burned. Time should be taken to examine the roots carefully to estimate degree of fungal or pest attack. On systems other than border culture, plant removal is carried out as is most practical.

Greenhouse Cleansing

A completely empty greenhouse can be cleaned out immediately after crop removal, although it is usual to wait until nearer the time of use again, as the glass can quickly become very dirty. Formaldehyde, cresylic acid or Jeyes Fluid can be used for washing down after fumigation, any time up to five or six weeks before the house is to be used again. Put it on with a sprayer, taking care to protect your eyes, and then hose the greenhouse down after a week or so. Alternatively with a long-handled brush you can brush on a good detergent or mild sterilant and then hose it off, trying to remove forcibly as much moss and algae as possible.

Note on Yields

Tomato yields differ enormously according to climatic pattern, variety, environmental conditions, planting density, situation, incidence of pests and disease and countless other factors. Commercial yields vary considerably according to degree of specialisation and in recent years with high-yielding varieties, yields have soared in commercial circles to an unprecedented level, to an average of around 30lb (14kg) or more per plant. It is stressed that this is on long-season specialised production and the average gardener should expect anything from 6 to 12lb (2.7 to 5.5kg) if tomato growing is to be considered worthwhile. One of the most critical issues, especially in amateur circles, is the avoidance of yield-reducing pests and diseases.

11

Diseases, Pests and Physiological or Nutritional Disorders

The tomato plant is unfortunately prone to a wide variety of troubles, many of which appear to assert themselves with some regularity. Undoubtedly the principle of growing the same crop successively in the same greenhouse, and often in the same soil, is partly responsible for this. This is why systems of culture involving fresh growing media are becoming so widely practised, although even with a clean start there are other troubles which are still persistent, no doubt because of the 'artificial' conditions in any greenhouse where plants are grown in limited quantities of growing medium. A plant with so many vital facets of growth requires a considerable degree of precision in culture, and obviously it is all too easy to relax attention.

Having painted this rather gloomy picture, I must also point out with some haste that certain troubles are so well known that it is relatively simple to take evasive or preventive action. For example, it is known that planting in cold soil checks the roots, allowing easy entry of parasitic fungi. Likewise it is readily appreciated that a highly humid atmosphere will induce the attack of botrytis (grey mould). Sufficient is also known about nutritional programmes for the grower to realise that a departure from the correct treatment will have repercussions. Plant breeders have done much to increase resistance to diseases, and this applies especially to leaf mould, vascular wilts and virus disease (TMV).

A catalogue of troubles must now necessarily follow, but at all times preventive measures will be emphasised.

One final point which must be made is that it is folly to try and take short cuts, or to imagine that if, for example, a root rot occurred severely in a border soil one year, it will vanish merely with the passage of time, some lime, manure and fertiliser. Organic principles of husbandry apart, which is a massive subject involving detailed study, I feel that it is as well to face up squarely to problems and sterilise effectively (*see* Chapter 12), re-soil, or go on to an alternative cultural method.

Very Important Note

In the course of dealing with the control of pests and diseases, reference will be made to various chemical preparations. It cannot be stressed too strongly that many of these chemicals are extremely potent poisons and must be used strictly as recommended, and kept safe in a locked cupboard. Gardeners are referred to the directory of gardening chemicals issued by the British Agrochemicals Association Ltd (*see* Appendix 4) which is regularly revised, and lists of trade names and chemical ingredients available to gardeners through retail establishments. Lists of chemicals for commercial growers appear in what is now called the 'Blue Book', entitled *Pesticides*. This is a list of all the approved chemicals available to commercial growers, but precise recommendations for their use is not given. It is available from the Ministry of Agriculture, Fisheries and Food or HM Stationery Office (*see* Appendix 4). This Blue Book does not replace the booklets issued for many years under the agricultural chemicals approval scheme entitled 'Approved products for farmers and growers'. It seems likely that publications will in time be available to give more precise information to commercial growers, who are in the meantime referred to the chemical companies supplying the products. The important thing is to read the label. Organic growers should refer to the Soil Association or similar bodies for advice in dealing with pests or diseases. Biological control of certain pests and diseases is now a practical reality.

Diagnostic Techniques

Plant pathology, entomology, and physiology (including nutrition) are highly specialised subjects requiring considerable detailed knowledge and, in many cases, highly complicated equipment. There are therefore obvious limits to what can be correctly diagnosed merely by the recognition of relatively standard symptoms. Nor is it the case that the symptoms exhibited always follow a single pattern or, for that matter, that only one trouble will affect one plant at a time. There would appear to be little rhyme or reason why some plants are attacked and others remain unaffected, although they may be growing in close proximity. On the other hand, trouble may be relatively simple and clear cut, and the use of a high-power magnifying glass may reveal much. Spore forms may also be remarkably distinctive and reference to a book on pathology will give good guidance. Where, however, there is any doubt about a malady, it is wrong to act impulsively and attempt a cure, as this could do more harm than good, and here it would be very wise to seek specialist advice.

DAMPING OFF

Symptoms Young plants fall over when $1^1/_2$–2in (3.5–5cm) high, the stem at soil level being shrivelled or 'pinched' in. Seedlings may seem unaffected only to collapse at a later stage with root rots as a secondary infection.

Agents involved Fungal parasites, phytophthora, pythium, corticium and others which gain entry either through the roots or the stem.

Prevention Avoid sources of infection such as dirty seedboxes, pots and soil. Clean, fresh peat, peat/sand mixes or properly prepared (sterilised) John Innes Seed Compost should be used, although the ammonia content of a soil-containing medium can injure the plants and afford easy entry for fungi, indicating that a soil-less medium is desirable. Here again, however, ammonia release from fertilisers such as hoof and horn can still be a problem. Dirty water can also carry infection and static tanks are a potent source of trouble.

Control Copper-based compounds, or more specifically Cheshunt Compound, are useful in preventing or limiting the spread of attack, but will not greatly help plants already attacked. Excessively high humidity should be avoided after the actual germination period is over. Where greenhouses are lined with polythene there can be damping-off problems unless ventilation is effective. All fungicides should be used according to directions.

Root Disorders

These attack portions of the plant below and at ground level since the root is affected and the uptake of water and nutrient is restricted according to the inroads made by the parasitic fungus involved. This could be one of a number of different species including colletotrichum, atramentarium, thielaviopsis basicola, rhizoctonia, pythium, phytophthora, didymella or fusarium. While accurate identification of the fungal parasite involved can be made by a pathologist, it is obviously difficult to be completely accurate by visual inspection only. Any form of root rot will cripple the growth of the plant to a greater or lesser degree, and identification of the parasite is of largely educational interest with respect to the present plant, but important, of course, for prevention and control for unaffected plants or for the future.

While a certain amount of control may be exercised over root rots, it is difficult to gain access to the fungal infection in the root tissues without damaging the plant cells. Systemic fungicides are now being used for certain aspects of disease control and these may offer great scope for the future. Resistance to certain troubles is also being bred into tomato varieties. Note also the use of rootstocks for grafting.

Types of Root Rot

Root rot Fine rootlets at or near soil level are attacked by the disease organism, leaving the main roots devoid of side roots or root hairs. The outer 'skin' of the root is usually attacked, allowing it to be removed, leaving behind the wiry vascular tissue. Intensity of attack varies considerably and only one section of the root may be attacked. A plant affected by root rot may continue to grow reasonably well, although wilting will occur when the temperature rises or when it changes quickly. The portion of root so far unaffected may in fact also continue to develop and to compensate in part for the damaged portion and this state of 'brinkmanship' may exist for the greater part of the season. Alternatively the progress of the disease may be rapid, as indicated by complete collapse of the vegetative portion of the plant. Damage of any kind to the root tissue – cold soil, over- or under-watering, excess fertiliser or the nibbling of pests such as wireworms, slaters or eelworm – obviously destroys the outside protective tissue of the root, allowing ready entry of the disease organisms.

Foot or collar rot The disease attacks at soil level and quite frequently the attack is connected with physical damage of some sort, including burning by excess fertiliser application. The stem at ground level will show a brown ring of tissue with shrivelled stem, and collapse of the plant could occur when sufficient inroads have been made into the vascular tissue.

Toe rot The extremities of the root are affected and, as with root rot, the restriction of growth is related to the severity of the attack. This is a frequent trouble arising at planting time, due to cold soil at lower depths. New adventitious roots will frequently be seen, initially forming as little lumps on the stem above soil level. Once these roots extend into the soil they may carry the plant on for a time, although collapse late in the season usually occurs.

Brown or corky root (sterile grey fungus) This is caused principally by the fungus *Pyrenochaeta terrestris* and results in a clubbed and brown appearance of the root, reducing its efficiency very considerably. It is frequently present in old tomato borders and very difficult to eliminate – even by sterilisation.

Prevention of Root Rot

Use of 'new' or properly sterilised soil is essential, especially if a previous crop has been seriously affected by one or other of the root rots, as spores or infected debris will remain in the soil and affect succeeding crops. 'New' soil means soil which has not been used for tomato (nor preferably, potato) cropping for a number of years, and there is every likelihood that such soils, provided they come up to the necessary physical and nutritional standard, will give excellent results, free of root rot, but there is no guarantee that this will be the case. The reason is that root rots (and for that matter other diseases) while relatively specific to tomatoes, are not entirely so, apart from which infection can frequently be air- or water-borne.

Sterilisation methods are dealt with in Chapter 12, yet unfortunately it seems very difficult to get rid of certain root rots (and other troubles), especially brown root, unless sterilisation is 100 per cent efficient, and this is hard to achieve in practice. Nevertheless, sterilisation techniques can on the whole be considered as effective, and where carried out correctly there is every likelihood that cropping results will be good, within the limits of the sterilisation process employed.

Control

Plants affected by root rots can be encouraged to stay alive if the progress of the root rot is checked, or limited to the affected area; and at least by using control methods the incidence of disease may be limited to as few plants as possible. Contact fungicidal chemicals such as dithane and household disinfectants such as Jeyes Fluid are frequently used and it is likely that others may be available shortly following the success of the systemic fungicide Benomyl for botrytis and other diseases (*see below*). In all cases use the chemicals as instructed. Preventive watering with these chemicals where root rots are suspected may also be helpful.

Spreading a layer of peat and lime (5–6oz or 140–170g ground limestone per bushel, or 36 litres), 'clean' soil, leaf mould or other compatible material will invariably induce the tomato plant to produce new adventitious roots at or above soil level, and these roots may sustain a plant suffering from some root debility for a period at any rate, depending on the severity of the attack. A plant badly affected by root rot may recover only very briefly, if indeed it manages to produce adventitious roots at all, before complete collapse of the root system occurs. On the other hand, mulching may help to sustain the plant sufficiently to produce a worthwhile crop, a lot depending on whether the new roots are able to cope with high temperatures if there is any very hot weather.

Combining mulching with shading is a frequent practice, painting the outside of the glass with lime and water or with a proprietary shading material, such as Varishade. I have found highly diluted emulsion paint useful. If the ventilation is reduced for a week or so and frequent damping down practised, the excessively humid conditions which develop will reduce the transpiration of the plant and encourage adventitious rooting. Adventitious roots once formed will of course respond to nutrient application just as 'real' roots do, provided the mulch is kept moist.

Mulching does in fact reduce moisture loss from the soil surface and can be carried out irrespective of whether or not there is incidence of root rots. In this case, however, straw is frequently used, which, in addition to reducing moisture loss, keeps the soil from splashing on to the plants.

The likelihood of root rots or other troubles (which will be discussed later) arising from infected soil, is one reason why growbags have become so popular. The same is true of other systems in commercial spheres.

VERTICILLIUM AND FUSARIUM WILTS

The fungal agent enters the plant usually through the roots and affects the vascular tissues, clogging these up by its exudations. Affected plants, usually 4–5ft (1.2–1.5m) tall and laden with fruit, will wilt when the temperature is sufficiently high to cause rapid transpiration, and frequently recover under cooler conditions. Cutting off the stem at ground level, then making a longitudinal cut along the width of the stem tissue, will show quite clearly the brown area.

Verticillium wilt is a disease more associated with low-temperature conditions in the north, while fusarium is more common in, but by no means confined to, the south. Apart from wilting, the leaves drop badly, accompanied usually by yellowing and withering of the lower leaves, often only at one side of the plant. Soils frequently build up an infection of verticillium or fusarium, which asserts itself in patches and spasmodically, and usually when the season is well advanced. Root rots can frequently occur in combination with wilts.

Prevention

The use of 'clean' or sterilised soil is essential, otherwise alternative cultural methods should be adopted. Avoid low temperatures and planting checks. Use grafted plant on rootstock KNVF or TMPVFN, the V and F referring to verticillium and fusarium respectively. Varieties are also available with inbuilt resistances (*see* Chapter 13).

Control

Once plants are seriously affected not a great deal can be done to alleviate the situation. Very badly affected plants are better removed. Indeed root rots frequently occur in badly debilitated plants in any case. Mulching, as described previously under root rots, accompanied by about 14 days at 77°F, may enable plants not only to survive, but in the case of verticillium wilt to 'cook' out the disease organisms involved. Benomyl has given encouraging results in the control of wilts.

DISEASES AFFECTING THE STEMS, LEAVES AND FRUIT

Two major diseases attack the stem of the tomato – didymella and botrytis – and both can cause immense damage.

Didymella (*Didymella lycopersici*)

This attacks the stem of a mature plant a few inches above soil level, causing brownish lesions dotted with shiny spores, which can be seen if examined with a lens. Leaf spotting can also occur, and in addition the fruit stems may rot, causing the fruit to drop. Damage ensues when the mycelium of the fungus cripples the vascular tissues. In a heavy attack there can be a tremendous toll of plants, yet there are occasions when only a few plants are affected. Infection arises from spores, and from contaminated seedboxes, soil, string, structure of the greenhouse, base walls, or anything which has been in contact with infected plants. Didymella generally tends to be spasmodic, although in certain areas it is a constantly recurring problem.

Prevention Immediate complete removal and burning of infected plants, coupled with thorough spraying of the remaining plants with dithane, concentrating the spray on the lower stem areas (other more potent chemicals were used for a time, but have now been withdrawn). Thorough hygiene of a routine nature is essential, particularly following an outbreak, and this involves thoroughly washing down the greenhouse structure, coupled with thorough soil sterilisation or the adoption of alternative cultural methods. It should be noted that even if this involves a 'new' growing medium, infection can still arise from other dirty sources. It is important that any doubtful plants at the end of the season be disposed of at once at some considerable distance from the greenhouses.

Botrytis Stem Rot *(Botrytis cinerea)*

The spores of grey botrytis mould abound in the atmosphere and gather readily on any receptive host. In the warm humid atmosphere of the greenhouse botrytis spores are in their element and it merely requires a dropped petal, the open scar of a removed leaf or side shoot, or rotting lower leaves, for the spores to germinate and start plundering, at a rate highly dependent on the humidity of the atmosphere and the softness of the tissue.

When air movement is restricted in any way, either by poor ventilation or dense foliage, conditions are ideal for the development of the fungus, sending its mycelium into the tissue and sporing profusely, as indicated by the mass of grey, dust-like spores which develop.

Botrytis also causes damage to the fruit by 'ghost spotting'. This happens when, in conditions of inadequate ventilation or low temperature at night, a droplet of moisture laden with spores falls on the fruit, and starts to attack the skin; it dries up again during the day – but obviously the fruit can become so badly marked that it loses its fresh appeal, and of course its sale value. The fruit is also attacked at the husk, causing it to drop, and flowers are also frequently attacked, rendering them useless.

Prevention Adequate ventilation and the avoidance of high humidity, especially at night (by ventilation and the use of night heat), timely defoliation, good balanced nutrition to keep plants hard rather than soft (some varieties have a considerably softer foliage than others, *eg* 'Moneymaker') and removal of all decayed leaves and debris. Fan ventilation has proved excellent for the prevention of botrytis because it can give positive air changes regardless of all weather conditions, but a time clock is required to give periodic night operation. Good hygiene pays big dividends; fallen leaves and other debris should never be left lying around.

Control Mild attacks by botrytis (before the disease makes massive inroads) can sometimes be effectively dealt with by scraping the stem down to clean tissue and, provided environmental conditions in the greenhouse are good and that some material such as lime and flowers of sulphur is used to dry the tissue, such control can be effective. Benomyl and copper compounds are useful. The worst damage usually occurs when the stem is attacked, usually at the point where a node sheath or leaf has been removed. Fungicidal smokes are especially useful if used at just the right time, before the disease reaches serious proportions. They can be very helpful in keeping fruit free from ghost spots. (Even creosote can be used on stems, this being painted on in neat form to the actual infected area on the stems.)

Leaf Mould Disease *(Cladosporium fulvum)*

This at one time was an accepted part of tomato culture; at various times of the season usually after about June, yellow patterns would appear on the upper surface of the older leaves, while on the underside felt-like patches of brown fungus will develop. The efficiency of the leaf is obviously impaired and the disease usually progresses until the whole plant is enveloped apart from the top portion which generally remains relatively clean. (This disease has a special personal significance for me as I became asthmatic when I entered a greenhouse where cladosporium existed in some quantity, an unfortunate allergy of which I was eventually cured by a course of injections.) Fortunately many varieties of tomato are now resistant to A, B, C and D strains of leaf mould. The situation regarding leaf mould resistance is constantly changing, due to mutations of the disease. Mild, damp areas, especially those on the western seaboard, favour the development of this mould.

Prevention Obviously the use of resistant varieties is the first line of defence, remembering the existence of different strains of cladosporium (A and B, and C). Adequate ventilation day and night, with heat at night to help air movement, will frequently keep cladosporium to the very minimum especially where non-resistant varieties are grown on account of their high quality and excellent cropping potential (*eg* 'Ailsa Craig' or 'Moneymaker') – *see* Chapter 13. Alternatively, chemical sprays can be used as a preventive measure, strictly according to directions. Aerosol packs of chemicals may also be used.

Control Mild attacks may be controlled or restricted by use of chemicals. Removal of the worst-affected leaves before application is also helpful.

Sclerotinia Stem Rot (*Sclerotinia sclerotiorum*)

The base of the stem is attacked and a white mould follows the appearance of black or brown lesions. When it makes sufficient inroads the fungus causes the plant to wilt or die. Careless fertiliser application or burning of the stem often initiates the attack. Black, shiny spores can clearly be seen through a magnifying lens.

Prevention and control Use a contact fungicide at an early stage of attack. Sterilise or change soil for future use.

Buck Eye Rot

This is typified by the formation on fruit of grey or reddish-brown patches with inner, circular rings, almost like the eye of an owl; infection occurs usually from soil splashing during careless watering.

Prevention and control All affected fruit must be removed, and care and attention given to watering. Spraying with dithane or other general fungicide may restrict the attack.

Potato Blight (*Phytophthora infestans*)

This is not really a problem under glass, except in areas where a lot of outdoor tomatoes are grown. Autumn tomato crops may be infected if grown out-of-doors for a period before being brought under glass. Symptoms are blackish-purple marginal areas on leaves, which eventually exhibit a white downy growth followed by serious defoliation. Fruit may also be attacked, causing dark brown blotches which penetrate into the flesh, rendering it inedible.

Prevention and control The BBC's blight forecast in farming programmes from about mid-June will advise when conditions are humid enough out-of-doors for the blight disease to develop. Spraying with a range of drenches can be done, but I feel that it is only necessary to do this with the outdoor crop or when plants are temporarily out-of-doors.

Virus Disease

Virus disease on tomatoes presents a very complicated picture, and only a pathologist using advanced techniques is able positively to identify virus diseases, although the more common virus disorders exhibit fairly clear symptoms. Virus diseases exist in the cells of the plant as ultra-microscopic, rod-shaped organisms which plunder the plants' protein content and upset its physiology in some way – usually by reducing photosynthesis or causing acute distortion, stunting or blotching. Virus is spread readily by sucking pests, hands, knives, physical contact of plants and by actual contact of the plant roots with affected debris in the soil. It is in fact very difficult to get rid of deep-seated virus infection in the border soil, as steaming is only usually effective to a limited depth in tomato borders. This is one reason why alternative cultural methods are practised.

Types of Virus Disease

Tomato mosaic virus (TMV) Pale yellow areas on the leaves of the plant may be accompanied by some destruction or roughening of the leaf according to the severity of the attack. Setting of fruit (the fertilisation process) may also be prevented, especially at the fourth to sixth truss stage and there may be blotchy ripening of existing fruit.

There can also be an area of dead cells around the vascular area under the skin of the fruit, resulting in 'bronzing'. The leaves of the plant may also become thin and develop a 'fern-like' appearance, and the top of the plant may become very hard and thin; there can be a general check to growth, again usually at the fourth to sixth truss stage.

Severe virus streak This stunts the plants badly and spreads rapidly. Dark brown streaks appear on the stems, which become hollow. Fruit may also become blotched.

Double streak Not normally a problem with glasshouse plants; it is more usual out-of-doors, when plants are badly stunted and die back.

Spotted wilt Here the upper leaves of the plant tend to curl downwards and inwards, exhibiting a bronze colouration, and fruit may exhibit concentric brown circles. This is a common malady of plants such as dahlias or chrysanthemums and is usually transmitted initially from them by sucking pests.

Cucumber mosaic Typical fern-leaf symptoms (*see* p168, tomato mosaic virus) develop. Apart from cucumbers, this is a malady of outdoor plants, transmission being by insects.

Prevention of Virus Disease

This is a difficult matter as the many sources of virus disease are very hard to eradicate. Obviously hygiene is of prime importance, washing down greenhouses carefully and carrying out heat-dependent methods of sterilisation methodically. Chemical sterilisation of the soil is of little avail, as it exercises little or no control on virus infection contained in root debris. A typical situation is that heat sterilisation clears the top 10–12in (25–30cm) of soil of virus infection yet when the plant roots penetrate beyond this, and they invariably do as the season progresses, they pick up infection. Alternative cultural methods using limited quantities of clean growing medium can ensure freedom from virus in the absence of contamination by either mechanical or insect agencies.

Virus-tested seed, which has also been heat- and chemically treated to free it from virus infection, is readily available. Care at the germination period will also minimise infection (*see* p83) and dipping fingers in 2 per cent trisodium phosphate or strong detergent during the pricking-off operation is a useful practice. Avoidance, as far as possible, of sudden temperature changes would appear from experimental work to help, as the 'check' period is found to coincide with virus onset; the principle behind this is that the virus is always present and makes progress when the plant is under strain. Sophisticated control equipment has been developed to help overcome 'check' periods.

Spraying with sugar or milk was for a time practised, this being to offset the plundering of the protein by the virus organisms, but it seems that normal foliar feeding can accomplish the same results. Experiments were carried out inoculating young plants from a cold-storage virus vaccine, thus bringing the 'check' period forward. Initially carried out on the Isle of Wight, there was considerable development of the technique. The introduction of virus-resistant and 'tolerant' varieties of tomatoes with resistant genes has raised considerable controversy owing to the rapid mutation of virus strains and the obvious long-term difficulty of using up resistant genes so that the plant breeder is left with no armoury against virus. Again, the problem of growing virus-tolerant varieties along with non-resistant varieties cannot be over emphasised, as the former may contain the virus and may pass it on whilst having no virus symptoms. Control of sucking pests is vital.

Control of Virus Disease

Only in severe cases should affected plants be removed and burned. It is doubtful whether there is any real value in removing TMV-affected plants. The practice of applying quick-acting, straight sources of nitrogen such as nitro-chalk or Nitram at about 1oz per sq yd ($33g/m^2$), or in liquid form at 1oz per gal (6g/litre) for containerised systems, is useful. The rules given for the prevention of the virus should serve as control measures for the future.

PESTS
Potato Cyst Eelworm or Nematode (PCN)

The major scourge of potatoes, this is also a serious pest of tomatoes (which are also solanaceous). Infestation occurs either from former potato land on which the greenhouse has been built, or from infected soil brought into it. The persistence of the eelworm is due to the protection afforded to the larvae by the tough-skinned swollen abdomens of the females; these cysts, as they are called, are very resistant to outside influences. The larvae are stimulated into activity by a solanaceous acid exudation (and possibly by other agencies).

Symptoms of infestation are the wilting of the plant in hot sun and general debility despite liberal feeding. Microscopic eelworm nibble at the root tissue (not the stem) reducing its efficiency and opening the way to fungal attack. Comparatively small initial eelworm attacks can quickly build up in severity and result in yellow patches on the lower leaves, followed by dry, dead patches. Confirmation of attack is the finding of minute cysts – white, yellow or orange according to their age – on the fine root hairs. Accurate eelworm counts can be carried out by the advisory services (*see* p197).

Eelworm counts are of course best carried out prior to using the soil for tomatoes.

Prevention and Control Completely effective soil sterilisation in greenhouse borders is difficult to achieve owing to the presence of eelworm in the lower depths of soil or greenhouse foundations. Sterilisation by heat will, however, keep the eelworm attack down to moderate proportions. Chemical sterilisation varies in its efficiency (*see* Chapter 12), a lot depending on the evenness of application and condition of the soil, but again it is usually possible to keep infestation to reasonable proportions.

Tomato grafting appears to give reasonable results, no doubt because of the vigour of the root system. The development of plants resistant to PCN is a reasonable possibility for the future. Alternative cultural methods do, of course, overcome the eelworm problem, provided there are no possible sources of infestation.

Watering with dilute Jeyes Fluid can be remarkably effective in containing the attack to reasonable proportions, and foliar feeding can also help to overcome debility by short-circuiting the roots. Mulching with peat can also help by providing the plant with sufficient new roots, as yet unaffected by eelworm, to sustain it. Combined D-D and solubilised cresylic acid treatment appears highly effective, the former chemical dealing with the lower depths of soil, and the latter with the upper layers. Amateur gardeners do not have access to these chemicals.

Root Knot Eelworm

Several different species of root knot eelworm, all belonging to the meloidogyne family, attack and enter the roots of the tomato, causing swellings, nodules and malformation. Roots are restricted in their efficiency according to the severity of the attack and mild attacks cause plant wilting in warm weather. Major onslaughts are disastrous, with severe wilting, yellowing leaves and death of plants.

Although not cyst forming, these eelworms exist in plant debris and are highly persistent. Preventive and control measures are as for PCN (*see above*). The letter 'N' in rootstock types refers to resistance to root knot eelworm, and in practice this resistance is highly effective.

Symphylids and Springtails

These affect mainly border-grown plants and are active insects of various colours, $1/4$in (6mm) in length, which can infest the roots of tomatoes, especially under warm, dry conditions early in the season. They are very mobile pests and move up and down according to soil temperature and conditions. They suck the sap of the roots causing loss of efficiency, and with their exudations cause distortion. They are more serious in the warmer southern counties than in the cooler north. Presence can be confirmed by taking some soil from the vicinity of the plant roots and placing this in water, when the insects will float to the surface.

Prevention and control Soil sterilisation is usually effective, although recurring infestations are likely because of the ability of these pests to move down below the level of sterilisation. Insecticidal drenches are reasonably effective if applied heavily.

Red Spider Mite (*Tetranychus urticae* or *cinnebarinus*)

A crippling pest, especially on certain soft-leaved varieties such as 'Moneymaker', which seems especially prone to attack. The tiny yellow or red mites concentrate on the underside of the leaves, causing acute loss of sap, speckling of leaves and eventually a dry, dirty appearance with a mass of webs. Countless generations develop in the year and overwinter in the greenhouse structure or any alternative host plants.

Prevention and control Chemical cleaning of the glasshouse structure, particularly the base walls, after first removing and burning affected plants, should be undertaken. Sulphur burning is advised.

A varying chemical programme is usually practised to avoid the buildup of resistance which can result from constant use of one chemical. As there are usually overlapping generations, control measures should be carried out on a concentrated basis over a short period. Sprays or aerosols (including smokes) may be used. Biological control is highly effective.

White Fly

This is one of the worst and most persistent pests. Eggs are laid by the waxy, white adult in circular clusters on the lower leaves, and after a nymph stage the adult emerges and feeds on the leaves, sucking sap and exuding a honeydew on which a fungus grows. Serious attacks damage plants severely and greatly restrict cropping. White fly is very difficult to control owing to the resistance to chemicals of the nymph stage.

Prevention and control As white fly overwinter on perennial plants and debris, very thorough cleaning of greenhouses is necessary. Decorative plants such as arum lilies or fuchsias overwintered in the greenhouse are frequently hosts to white fly.

Whatever insecticide is selected, it is advisable not only to vary the treatment, but to ensure that two or three applications are given in quick succession. It is advisable to spray the soil in the morning to kill off any surviving flies. Biological control is worth considering, although there are still some problems in this direction.

Thrips and Aphids

Many different species can attack tomatoes, both at the young stage when they cause severe distortion and growth restrictions, and later in the season. Aphids cause distortion with yellow patches on leaves and white blotches on fruit. They also exude honeydew. Thrips cause silvery blotches. Both can spread viral diseases.

Prevention and control Use of insecticides, varying the type to avoid building up resistances, especially as many types of aphid seem already to have developed resistance to many insecticides.

Tomato Leafminer

This is a common pest and, like all leafminers, it tunnels into the leaf structure leaving a trail of destruction.

Prevention and control Remove infested leaves and burn; make frequent use of insecticides.

Tomato Moth

This can be a damaging pest, the green caterpillars nibbling at the leaves and stems and eating holes in the fruit. Eggs are laid in batches on the underside of leaves.

Prevention and control Good hygiene and early use of insecticides.

Miscellaneous Pests

Woodlice The familiar flat 'slaters' attack young or older plants at the base of the stems. Special insecticidal dusts can be used, failing which place sections of turnip or potato around the plants and burn congregating woodlice, preferably with a flamegun or blowlamp.

Mice Always a problem with any crop, they can eat seed or nibble at young plants. Trap or bait.

Wireworms Common on new pastureland, the familiar wireworms enter the main stem and tunnel up the centre. Use insecticidal dusts or sterilise the soil.

Millipedes Curled up like a coiled spring, these can be a nuisance if present in sufficient numbers, but can be controlled with an insecticidal drench.

PESTS AND DISEASES SUMMARY

Readers should also consult the chart on mineral and physiological disorders on pages 170–2 as there may frequently be a complex of conditions. It should be noted that changing to a different cultural system and new growing medium largely overcomes many pest and disease problems.

Mineral Disorders

Mineral disorders (*see* table pp170–1) can arise very frequently under the intensive cultural conditions practised in greenhouses, and perhaps more especially where a soil-less medium is used. A sensible approach to tomato nutrition can help in the avoidance of problems, but with the best will in the world disorders can occur. Conversely it is all too easy to become supersensitive to mineral disorders and blame them for every growth irregularity, when in fact it could be a pest, disease, water or temperature problem. The accurate diagnosis of mineral deficiency is not simple and the table following deals with the more general and easily recognisable symptoms. (*See* Chapter 3 for details of the major element, their deficiency and excess.)

Physiological Troubles

Physiological troubles (*see* table pp171–2) do not appear to be directly related to a specific pest, disease or mineral disorder and so are called 'physiological'. Excess or insufficient water, the effect of temperature extremes, lack of air in the growing medium because of compaction, are frequent causes. The point must be made, however, that it is wrong to try and think in too compartmentalised a manner, as physiological disorders may have pest, disease or nutritional implications.

Important Note

Tomatoes are highly susceptible to contamination from weedkilling hormone materials which gain entry through vents etc. Leaves go nettle-like and fruit becomes pear-shaped with a 'carbolic' taste. Metham-sodium sterilants may also cause acute leaf distortion in young plants, if not fully dissipated from the growing medium.

Pests and Diseases Summary

Trouble	Symptoms	Cause	Control
Damping off	Young seedlings keel over at soil level.	Use of incorrectly sterilised or 'dirty' soil or containers. Ammonia release may induce damage.	Use clean containers and soil. Apply copper-based Cheshunt Compound.
Root rots: root, foot, toe, and corky root rot	Plants wilt and may eventually die, depending on severity of attack. Roots brown and dried looking.	Infected soil or cold checks. Young plants may have had infection from propagating stage.	Remove infected plants. Sterilise soil for future or adopt alternative cultural systems. Use of fungicide in liquid form may limit attack. Mulching is useful for producing new adventitious roots at soil level.
Wilts: verticillium and fusarium	Plants wilt badly in hot sun but can recover at night. Advanced symptoms – leaves yellow and hanging, vascular tissue seen to be brown if affected plant cut at ground level.	Infected soil.	Mulching and sterilising is the only real way of overcoming attack. 3 weeks at 77°F (25°C) for verticillium only. Use grafted plants. Resistant varieties also available.

Trouble	Symptoms	Cause	Control
Diseases affecting stem, leaves and fruit:			
Didymella	Plants show diseased lesions a few inches above ground level and wilt and die.	Infected soil.	Remove affected plants and spray remainder.
Botrytis	Stem rot. Ghost spotting of fruit. Leaves rot and fruit drops due to attack at husk.	Air-borne infection.	Give adequate ventilation, especially at night, to avoid high humidity. Scrape clean and paint with fungicide or creosote. Use aerosols or spray regularly with Benlate.
Leaf mould	Leaves yellow, spotted with brown felt-like fungal growth on the underside.	Air-borne infection.	Give adequate ventilation, especially at night. Use fungicidal sprays. Use resistant varieties.
Sclerotinia stem rot	Base of stem attacked.	Soil-borne infection.	Use fungicidal wash. Sterilise soil for future.
Buck eye rot	Diseased 'eyes' in fruit.	Soil-borne infection.	Remove all diseased fruit and take care with watering. Spray with chemicals.
Potato blight	Grey blotches on leaves. Sometimes black areas on fruit. Crops rarely affected under glass.	Air-borne infection.	Preventive sprays with fungicides.
Virus diseases:			
TMV (tomato mosaic virus)	Mottling of leaves. Bad setting. Bronzing of fruit.	Transmitted from soil, debris and seed etc.	Give nitro-chalk at 1oz per sq yd (33g/m^2). Grow resistant (or tolerant) varieties.
Severe streak and double streak	Markings on stem and dieback of plant.	Transmitted from soil, debris and seed etc.	Remove affected plants and burn.
Spotted wilt	Top of plant turns down. Fruit has concentric brown circles.	Transmitted from plant remains etc.	Remove badly infected plants and burn.
Cucumber mosaic	Fern-leaf symptoms of leaves (do not confuse with hormone damage, for which see p 167).	Transmitted by sucking pests.	Remove severely affected plants and keep weeds down in greenhouse.

Trouble	Symptoms	Cause	Control
Pests:			
Potato cyst eelworm or nematodes (PCN).	Wilting, blotching and yellowing of lower leaves.	Infection arising from cysts in soil that was previously used for potato culture.	Sterilisation of soil. Watering with chemicals. Mulching and foliar feeding.
Root knot eelworm	Wilting and general debility. Roots affected with swellings.	Soil-borne infestation.	Sterilisation or use of rootstock. Mulching. Soil drenches.
Symphylids and springtails	Very small insects in clusters on roots.	Deep-seated infestation.	Sterilisation. Soil drenches.
Spider mite	Tiny little brown or red spiders on underside of leaves.	Arising from overwintering mites in greenhouse.	Chemical sprays or aerosols, applied concentrated over a period. Biological control.
White fly	White flies feeding on leaves, exuding honeydew which develops brown/black fungal growth.	Overwinters in vegetative tissue or in cracks.	Sprays or aerosols concentrated over a period. Biological control.
Thrips and aphids	Various types of greenfly and sucking pest, all sucking sap and causing general debility.	Infestation arises from various sources frequently from outside crops.	Sprays and aerosols applied concentrated over a period, varying the chemicals.
Tomato leafminer	Tunnelling of leaves.	Infestation usually imported from outside crops.	Pick off affected leaves and apply preventive insecticide.
Tomato moth	Green caterpillar eats into stems, leaves and fruit.	Not a frequent pest, appearing spasmodically.	Apply insecticide.
Woodlice	Attack base of stem.	Infestation arises from various sources.	Insecticidal dusts or burning of congregating insects.
Mice	Eat seed or nibble young plants.	Infestation arises from various sources.	Trap or bait at first signs.
Wireworms	Enter main stem and tunnel up centre.	Infestation arises from recent pastureland.	Insecticidal dusts or soil sterilisation.
Millipedes	Affect roots, causing wilting.		Insecticidal drenches.

Mineral Disorders		
Symptoms	*Cause*	*Cure*
Small pale leaves, thickened and twisted. Cracks on leaves near veins. Growing point dies, side shoots develop bushy plant, slow development of fruit.	Boron deficiency	Use boron at 0.03oz/sq yd (1g/m^2).
Small greyish green/violet leaves curling downward. Old leaves fall off. Thin stems, flowering delayed, slow development of fruit.	Phosphorus deficiency	Add triple super-phosphates at 1.5oz/sq yd (50g/m^2).
Leaf edges turn yellow and turn down, stems turn down. Uneven or hollow fruit development.	Potassium deficiency	Use potassium nitrate at 0.6oz/sq yd (20g/m^2).
Leaf edges turn brown. Thin tip growth, black base to fruit ('black bottom').	Calcium deficiency	Analyse calcium levels. Add dolomitic lime at 3oz/sq yd (100g/m^2): raise nitrogen level.
Young leaves wither, leaf tips dry up and twist. Stems thin and woody.	Copper deficiency	Use copper sulphate at 0.06oz/sq yd (2g/m^2).
Pale colour between veins on older leaves. Stems narrow. Flowers pale. Low yields.	Magnesium deficiency	Use magnesium sulphate at 0.3oz/sq yd (10g/m^2).
Leaves light in colour, patchy. Marbled mottling effect.	Manganese or iron deficiency	Analyse for deficiencies. For iron use iron chelate at 0.09oz/sq yd (3g/m^2). For manganese use magnesium sulphate at 0.03oz/sq yd (1g/m^2).
Light green leaves, veins on lower surface purple. Stems thin and stiff.	Sulphur deficiency	Analyse before adding sulphur.
Leaves small and pale all over. Fruit small, pale green before ripening, deep red when ripe.	Nitrogen deficiency	Add nitrogenous feed.
Leaves large and deep green. Fruit large and slow to ripen. Thick stems.	Nitrogen excess	Decrease nitrogen feed, increase potash.

Physiological Disorders		
Symptoms	*Main cause*	*Corrective treatment (if any)*
Blotchy ripening Fruit showing light patches which fail to ripen.	Irregular watering and feeding resulting in variable salt content in soil.	Avoid irregular watering, feeding and temperature as far as this is practical. Some varieties are worse than others, especially those in the 'vigorous' categories.
Greenback The shoulder of the fruit remains green.	Common with greenback varieties such as 'Ailsa Craig' and its offspring. 'Moneymaker' types were developed to avoid this disorder. Excess sunlight, lack of potash, or too hard defoliation can induce greenback.	Avoid over-defoliation. Shade in extreme instances when very hot weather persists. Step up potash application.
Blossom end rot or 'black bottoms' The bottom end of fruit develops an area of cell necrosis which turns brown or black.	Due to high salt concentration in growing medium, also calcium deficiency. Lack of water also critical at early stages of growth. Can be bad in limited quantities of growing medium (eg growbags).	Regular water applications. Flush out salts and start again with a balanced feeding programme. Spraying foliage with dilute calcium sulphide could help.
Bronzing Dead layer of cells immediately below skin.	Excessively high daytime temperatures. Could also be due to virus or to boron deficiency; some confusion still exists as to the exact cause.	Avoid high daytime temperatures and check for other troubles. The trouble seldom persists for more than a few trusses.
Fruit Splitting Fruit splits or cracks.	Due to irregular water uptake or occasionally to varying temperatures. A frequent trouble in cold houses when fruit has been a long time developing and has grown a tough skin.	Even up temperatures as far as possible, shading if necessary to avoid excess daytime temperatures. Go on to a much more regular watering pattern.
Oedema Nodules appear as bumps or blotches on stems. Transpiration cannot take place rapidly enough through leaves.	Due generally to continuous excess humidity. Common in container-growing systems where excess water lies about between troughs or containers.	Reduce humidity by getting rid of excess water. Adequate ventilation especially at night.

Symptoms	Cause	Cure
Leaf curling Leaves develop excessive curl upwards, especially older ones.	Due to large variation in temperatures between day and night (the plant being unable to cope with surplus carbohydrates).	Adjust day/night temperature differential.
Silvering Foliage turns light in colour on a portion of the plant; half the leaves may be affected.	This is thought to be a genetic disorder associated with tissue layers and may correct itself or persist.	Select varieties which are not so susceptible.

Flower Disorders		
Symptoms	*Cause*	*Cure*
Dry set Pollen goes dry on stigma preventing fertilisation, leaving 'pin-head' fruits.	High temperatures, dry air, energy lag in plant resulting in 'check' period when infertile pollen may be produced. Virus disease can also cause poor setting.	Attempt to improve control of environment and check for virus.
Flower abortion Fertilisation occurs but abortion also occurs, ie the process of fruit development subsequent to fertilisation is arrested. Generally in first or second truss of fruit and only 'chat' fruits develop.	Considerable research is still being carried out on this phenomenon. It is thought to be related to light input (light intensity) or day/night temperature relationship, which produces flowers bearing pollen not fully viable. Vegetative development of young plants is obviously a vital factor and this has been discussed in earlier chapters.	Propagation regime should be controlled as far as this is possible. The use of artificial light, either supplementary or in a growing room, where there is some standardisation of conditions under which early flower trusses are laid down. (This of course occurs at a very early stage and the first and possibly the second trusses are initiated during the light-treatment period.)
'Missing' flowers Truss forms but flowers either do not appear or only open partially.	Due largely to excess supplies of nitrogen and connected with low salt content of soil. Low night/ high day temperatures and poor light intensities are contributory.	Apply potash to harden growth and adjust salt concentration in soil. Balance up day and night temperatures.
Flower drop Flowers drop off at 'knuckle'	Due to lack of water at roots, dry atmosphere or high salt concentration in soil.	Check water and feed applications and improve environmental control.

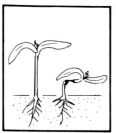

DAMPING OFF Causes
seedlings to keel over and
die; black withering on stem

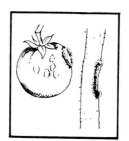

GREY MOULD (Botrytis)
Causes stem rot and ghost spotting
on fruits – finally shows as grey mould

LEAF MOULD
Brown fungal growth on
leaf under surface, yellow above

POTATO BLIGHT
Grey blotches on leaves, black
pitted spots on fruits

TOMATO MOSAIC VIRUS
Causes fern-like distortion of
leaves (compare with healthy
leaf on right)

RED SPIDER MITE Tiny
red mites cause yellow flecking
to leaf and webbing

WHITE FLY These suck
sap and exude honeydew;
easily seen

APHIDS Cause leaf
distortion and exude
honeydew

LEAFMINER
White pattern on leaf

GREENBACK
A hard green rim to tomato
just below the calyx

BLOSSOM END ROT (Black bottom)
A sunken grey-black rot
at blossom end of the tomato;
black seeds also likely

SPLITTING
Splits in side wall of tomato
just before ripening

12

Sterilisation of Soil and Other Growing Media

Any system of monoculture involving successive short-term crops gives rise to a variety of disorders of which nutritional imbalance is one. Each crop makes its special demands on available major and trace nutrients. In addition plant toxins, and acids secreted by all growing plants, accumulate and may influence adversely the micro-organism population of the soil or growing medium (soil-less media, although relatively sterile initially, rapidly become invaded by micro-organisms), which has nutritional repercussions. Antagonism and competition can also develop between the micro-organisms, beneficial groups frequently being repressed by non-beneficial ones. The buildup of fungal diseases and harmful pests specific to any crop, in this case tomatoes, is of course a major problem. Matters are not helped by the widespread use of chemical fertilisers, which give rise to further complications in the buildup of toxic residues.

The simple term for such a motley collection of problems is 'soil sickness' and it is certain that organic principles of husbandry could do much to prevent it, always provided of course that one is prepared to wait until troubles have been overcome – but this is not always practicable, especially in commercial circles.

Soil sterilisation, or more accurately pasteurisation, either by heat or chemical means, endeavours to rectify these ills and leave the beneficial elements to function. Pasteurisation is, technically speaking, different from complete sterilisation – which renders a medium sterile, not a desirable state of affairs for a soil-containing medium, but the term soil sterilisation is nevertheless commonly used to mean pasteurisation. Weeds in both vegetative and seed form should be killed by effective sterilisation. Sterilised soil is not immunised in any way, and indeed is perhaps more prone to re-infection by troubles than one which is not sterilised. Sterilisation by the use of heat is, however, far from being an exact technique and has definite limitations unless adequate temperatures are achieved for a suitable period of time and all parts of the growing medium are equally sterilised – simple in theory but difficult in practice. This is especially necessary in the control of virus diseases and potato cyst eelworm, now called potato cyst nematode (PCN). Ammonia release is also a problem in soil-based media, as the main groups of bacteria left unscathed are thick-walled ammonia and nitrogen-forming types.

The problems of sterilisation, coupled with the shortage of reliable and consistent supplies of soil, are the main reasons why such widespread use has been made in recent years of soil-less media, where the basic ingredients do not normally require sterilisation if fresh supplies are used on a regular basis.

The last few years have seen considerable changes in sterilisation techniques; the following sections give a brief résumé of modern methods. It must be appreciated that certain methods are obviously impossible in amateur circles, both in respect of the necessary equipment and because of the undesirability of using certain chemicals – legislation existing in the latter case.

HEAT STERILISATION

Several methods of heat sterilisation are practised, basically with the objective of bringing the soil or growing medium uniformly to a temperature sufficiently high and for a long enough period to kill off harmful organisms, while leaving beneficial types unharmed. The period of heat should not be prolonged enough to upset the nutritional balance. The temperature of 160–70°F (71–7°C) is generally accepted as being effective for most harmful organisms, although virus-infected debris and possibly eelworm cysts may remain unscathed, necessitating higher temperatures, of 180–90°F (82–7°C), as confirmed by a soil thermometer. (Higher temperatures are however frequently advised.)

The Hoddesdon Method

This method was developed at the Cheshunt Research Station (since closed). It involves leading pressurised steam into perforated pipes placed 10–12in (25–30cm) below the soil, which should preferably be moist and friable. A PVC sheet is placed on top of the soil and steam applied for 15–20 minutes or longer until the top of the soil has reached 180–90°F (92–7°C). Spikes or harrow grids are also employed, the latter being pulled through the soil by an automatic winch.

Sheet Steaming

Developed originally in the Netherlands and modified by H.B. Wright of Cottingham, this process involves leading the pressurised steam into either a perforated hose or a 'coffin'-type box with outlet holes, and under layers of heavy-grade PVC sheeting secured at the edges by sandbags or other means. The sheet billows up and the steam condenses on the soil surface, the heat travelling downwards in bands. Heat penetration depends both on soil type and method of cultivation, the best penetration being where soil is of a porous type, or rendered so by rough digging or some other method which does not make the soil too fine. Soil temperature must be accurately measured by side or oblique insertion of a soil thermometer. It can take several hours for the steam to penetrate deep enough, and in an effort to improve penetration stronger PVC sheeting is often used or nylon net is put over the PVC. Methods involving the using of air and steam to bring the temperatures down sufficiently to avoid over-sterilisation of the soil surface are also practised. Sheet steaming has found favour with growers of lettuce, chrysanthemum and short-term tomato crops, although results have been excellent in many instances for long-term tomato crops, much depending again on the presence or otherwise of deep-seated troubles. The main advantage of sheet steaming is the saving in labour. Portable steam-raising equipment now on the market is useful for dealing with limited areas. Rockwool is now steamed by various methods.

Low-pressure Steaming and Other Methods

Few smaller growers or amateur gardeners have facilities for producing pressurised steam in sufficient quantity for effective sterilisation, although small quantities of soil for potting purposes or the preparation of composts can be steamed with a small electric steam steriliser. Low-pressure steaming is, however, an acceptable proposition, whereby water is boiled below a per- forated tray which contains the soil, a PVC sheet again being used to cover the soil. Low-pressure sterilisation can be slow, according to soil type and moisture content, it being highly important to check the temperature achieved on the soil surface.

Drenching shallow layers of soil with boiling water and covering immedi- ately with clean sacks has much to commend it, as also has the suspension of small quantities of soil in a sack over boiling water. Soil so treated can be reasonably well sterilised.

Dry Heat Sterilisation

This can take several forms, the most basic being the use of a fire over which a sheet of corrugated iron or other metal is then placed and the soil spread in shallow layers above the main source of the heat. It helps if the soil is fairly wet, and care must be taken not to over-sterilise the soil or burn off the organic content, as this will completely destroy soil structure as well as rendering it sterile. A flame gun can also be used to the same effect for limited quantities of soil spread in a shallow layer on a clean surface.

Rotary drum sterilisers are widely used on commercial holdings and by local authorities. The soil is put in at one end of the drum which, by rotating, allows the soil to fall several times through a flame. The angle of the drum determines the rate at which the soil is ejected from the other end of the drum. Care must be taken that the soil is sufficiently dry, otherwise it can come through improperly sterilised, frequently 'balling' in the process. It is highly important to check the temperature of the ejected soil to ensure that it comes out at a uniform 160–70°F (71–7°C) or higher if virus or eelworm control is sought. Electric sterilisers operating on the panel element system are highly efficient and available in several sizes. Perlite and vermiculite are frequently sterilised by both rotary drum and panel element systems.

CHEMICAL STERILISATION

Various chemicals are used for sterilisation and for economic reasons have become very popular in commercial spheres. Chemicals are also useful for the amateur gardener, but great care must be taken to ensure that they are properly used. The main drawback to chemical sterilisation is that the fumes are toxic to young plants, which raises problems in 'mixed' greenhouses.

To be effective, chemicals must give off gas of sufficient toxicity and concentration to be capable of destroying pests, diseases and weeds, and yet they must leave the beneficial organisms unharmed. The efficiency of chemicals varies greatly, not only according to their precise chemical content, but according to the condition of the soil, its moisture content and, perhaps more important, prevailing temperature. Even distribution throughout the soil being sterilised is also highly important.

Formaldehyde

This has a good effect on mild fungal diseases, but is relatively ineffective against many pests. It is used at a strength of 1 part formalin 38–40 per cent in 49 parts water (approximately 12 pints in 6gal, or 1 litre in 49 litres) and the soil is drenched thoroughly, about 5gal per sq yd (27 litres/m^2) being required (to 9in or 22cm depth). The soil is ready for use in 20–40 days according to temperature, which must be sufficiently high (50–55°F, 10–13°C) otherwise the formaldehyde will merely polymerise.

Phenol and Other Chemicals

Various phenols are available, including cresylic acid, and should be used according to directions, but broadly in a similar way to formaldehyde, the soil being ready for use in 18–20 days. Action on the soil is largely insecticidal, but there is also some fungicidal action. Usually about 5–6gal of the prepared solution is required per sq yd (27.31 litres/m^2).

Other chemicals are used *commercially* and include D-D (principally on nematodes) and carbon bisulphide – both of these being injected into the soil – dithane, chloropicrin, methyl bromide and metham-sodium. The metham-sodium sterilants are widely used commercially, principally now as Dazomet which is a powdered or prilled form. (Methyl isothyiocyanate (Basamid), a slightly different formulation, is available – in 5kg packs only – from horticultural suppliers (*not* retail garden centres)). The metham-sodiums have a wide control spectrum. These chemicals must be used strictly according to directions, which generally state that the soil should be cultivated, the sterilants applied and, with the powdered or prilled form, rotovated in before 'sealing' with water. For them to be effective the temperature of the soil should ideally be above 49–50°F (9.5°C), but this temperature has in recent years been modified. In my personal experience however the higher the soil temperature after application the better. After a few weeks the soil should be rotary cultivated or forked on several occasions to release the fumes and prevent damage to plants. Heaps of potting soil can of course be treated in a similar manner. Methyl bromide has found increasing favour in recent years, due to its excellent action on pests and disease, and also to its rapid dissipation.

Methyl bromide must be applied by a contractor, and seepage into drains must be avoided.

Sterilisation Chart							
Material	Root eelworm	Root rots	Wilt diseases	Virus (TMV)	Damping-off disease	Weeds	Days between treatment and planting
Steam (including properly applied dry heat and hot water) usually at 180°F (82°C)	C	C	C	C (good at 194°F/ 90°C)	C	C	7–14
Metham-sodium* (results variable)†	C	C	P	X	C	C	40
For-maldehyde	X	P	P (Good at 60°F/ 16°C)	X	P	X	20–40
Dithane	X	P	X	X	P	X	3–14
Cresylic acid	P	X	P	X	P	X	18–20
D–D†	C	X	X	X	X	X	40
Carbon bisulphide (by injection)†	C	X	X	X	X	X	7
Methyl bromide †	C	C	P	X	C	C	4
Chloropicrin †	X	C	C	X	C	X	20

Key　C = control　　　　　* = only certain forms may be available to amateurs
　　　P = partial control　　† = not available to amateurs
　　　X = no control

Note seedboxes, pots etc, should also be sterilised, although with the increasing use of plastics, washing out with hot water containing a little detergent is usually sufficient.

Important Note

The instructions regarding the use of chemicals generally has been subject to considerable legislation in recent years, restricting the sale of products to commercial growers and amateur gardeners. Availability or otherwise of chemicals referred to above should therefore be ascertained from suppliers.

13

Tomato Varieties

This list of varieties makes no claim to being exhaustive. It is taken with grateful acknowledgement from the 1989 seed catalogues of D.T.Brown and Co Ltd and Sutton Seeds Ltd (*see* Appendix 4 for addresses).

The combined list is considered reasonably representative of what varieties are both available and grown in Britain at the present time. Commercially, the top sellers would appear to be 'Abunda', 'Calypso', 'Goldstar' and 'Turbo' in that order, with the variety 'Counter' replacing 'Sonatine'.

In retail terms 'Abunda', 'Curabel' and 'Arasta' are popular but in garden centres there are many gardeners still asking for older varieties such as 'Ailsa Craig', 'Moneymaker' and 'Alicante' although these are tending to be ousted because they do not have resistance to certain diseases. The important thing is to try a few varieties and concentrate on the one which suits your conditions best. This is especially true of the commercial grower who will usually get guidance in this direction from other commercial growers in the area. Up-to-date seed catalogues should always be consulted as the situation regarding varieties is a constantly changing one.

VARIETIES LIST
F1 Hybrids TMV Resistant

Abunda Outstanding, with firm, well-rounded fruits, and short sturdy trusses. Sets well in short-day situation.

Allegro A new variety, from Bruinsma.

Calypso Longer jointed than 'Abunda', but excellent fruit quality and long shelf-life.

Counter A high-yielding and early variety.

Curabel The qualities of 'Cura', together with fusarium and cladosporium A, B and C resistance. Suits heated or cold houses.

Danny Early, with easy fruit setting and high yield. Use for medium-early to late crops. Open habit and short jointed.

Estrella High-grade producer. Resistant to fusarium 1, cladosporium A, B and C, and verticillium.

Goldstar High average weight of fruit, with good shape, colour and firmness. Matures later than Abunda. Valuable as heated crop, interplanted with an earlier crop. Resistant to silvering.

Ida Early ripening, useful for cold houses. Compact habit and close jointed. Cladosporium and fusarium resistant.

Ostona Early variety. Cladosporium 1, 2, 3 and 4 and fusarium resistant.

Rapide Cladosporium 1, 2, 3, 4, 5, verticillium and fusarium resistant. Excellent main crop variety.

Shirley Early, short-jointed variety of improved 'Cura'. Good-shaped fruits, and heavy yields.

Sonatine A leading variety: raisers' packets only.

Tornado Early and compact growing. Suits British summers. Sweet-flavoured, thin-skinned fruits.

Turbo Versatile variety, suiting early cropping and interplanting when used as late cold crop.

Wilset Early, compact habit. Sets well in low or high temperature. Round, firm fruit, of good colour.

Other F1 Hybrids

Arasta Early and non-greenback. Cladosporium A, B and C resistant.

Eurocross BB Non-greenback with large fruit.

Grenadier Early variety. Fusarium resistant.

Herald Early, tall-growing and vigorous. Greenback-free.

Sweet 100 An excellent cherry variety.

F1 Hybrid Beefsteak Varieties

Dombito Improved beefsteak type. Firm and fleshy fruits.

Dona New variety, with large, firm fruits. Short-jointed and strong-growing. Verticillium and fusarium resistant.

F1 Hybrid Outdoor Variety

Alfresco Raise under glass late March, plant out from mid-May. Tolerant of bad weather. Vigorous and compact.

F1 Hybrid Rootstock for Grafting

KVNF The normal rootstock used.

TMPFVN Hires

Signal For grafting TMV varieties. Slower germination than normal varieties.

Straight Varieties

Ailsa Craig Carefully re-selected stock.

Alicante Early, greenback-free variety.

Best of All Large, fleshy fruits with few seeds.

Gardeners' Delight Numerous, small fruits. Sweet flavour.

Golden Sunrise A variety with attractive yellow fruit.

Harbinger Ripens early. Crops well. Popular, with good flavour.

Marmande Outdoor Continental variety. Firm flesh, few seeds, irregular fruits. Not for growing under glass.

Moneymaker/Moneycross Selection Cladosporium resistant.

Moneymaker Outstanding quality.

Outdoor Bush Varieties

French Cross High-yielding. Vigorous, with many trusses. Large, good-flavoured fruits.

Red Alert Early maturing. Heavy crop of small fruits.

Sigmabush Early, with good quality and good yield. Open habit.

The Amateur Not under glass before April. Needs no staking or pinching.

Tornado Early and compact-growing. Suits British summers. Sweet-flavoured, thin-skinned fruits.

Unusual Tomatoes

Tiny Tim Ideal for pots.

Totem Ideal dwarf for pots.

14

Outdoor Tomatoes

The success of tomatoes grown entirely out of doors, apart from the propagation period, is related entirely to weather pattern as influenced by latitude, exposure and type of season. In many years it is impossible to produce ripe fruit outdoors in many areas of Britain. Often protection must be provided by means of cloches, frames or polythene shelters. However, the availability of varieties of prostrate growing habit and those with the ability to grow and produce ripe fruit under lower temperature regimes, has given a boost to the growing of tomatoes out-of-doors.

Areas of Britain such as the south-coast region, including the south-east corner round to Essex, are perhaps the ideal areas for outdoor culture, and success has also been achieved by gardeners in other eastern counties such as Norfolk. The Channel Islands, and Jersey in particular, have long grown outdoor tomatoes commercially, although in recent years even Jersey has tended, like its sister island Guernsey, to move more towards culture of tomatoes under glass because of the unpredictable nature of the outdoor crop.

PRE-PLANTING PROCEDURES
Site Selection

Within the area available, a site should be selected which offers protection from wind and receives the maximum amount of sun. Should a south-facing border in front of a tall wall be available, this is ideal. Alternatively, select the best open site there is, taking into account such factors as wind. The use of portable shelter materials can often improve facilities enormously.

Soil Preparation

The instructions in each chapter relating to the nutrition of tomatoes, while relevant, are not all completely applicable. Outdoor tomatoes are of remarkably short-term nature and therefore nutrient uptake is much less than for a glasshouse crop. Conversely, however, there is not so much control of water application, and there could be excessive leaching out of nutrients during wet spells of weather. Soil texture and drainage should be good, and well-rotted FYM or peat should be applied in sufficient quantities to bring about the necessary improvement, coupled with deep digging to improve drainage. Quantities of FYM can be in the region of one barrowload per 6–8sq yd (7m²), and peat in almost unlimited quantities, provided the necessary amount of lime is used to offset its acidity.

Alternatively special raised beds can be prepared, using compost (John Innes Potting No 2 type) or a soil-less equivalent in ridges, roughly on the basis of half a bushel (18 litres) a plant – on top of polythene, if necessary, where pests or diseases are likely to be a problem. Growing in polythene-lined trenches filled with soil-less media can also be worth considering, provided there are drainage facilities. The same is true of growbags.

Tomatoes, although a short-term crop out-of-doors, are still susceptible to various maladies, potato cyst eelworm being a particularly likely pest in gardens where potatoes have been grown. Wireworms can also be trouble-some. While chemical sterilisation of soil out-of-doors is perfectly possible, and is practised commercially in Jersey, it is seldom practical in the average garden. A measure of crop rotation should, however, be possible. But, obviously, if there is difficulty about this the alternative cultural systems referred to throughout the book can be considered, on the lines described for indoor systems. Organic enthusiasts will be using trenches of compost.

Application of Lime

The adjustment of the pH to around the 6.5 level should be carried out, avoiding direct contact between FYM and lime and applying the lime in time to allow the pH figure to rise before planting. In areas of calcium soil no lime will of course be needed and there is much virtue in adding copious amounts of peat to reduce the pH sufficiently to avoid iron-deficiency problems.

Application of Base Feeds and Final Preparation of the Soil

Where special composts or organic methods are not being adapted, a base feed should be applied at 6–8oz per square yard (200–230g/m²), selecting one of medium-potash content. Base feeds should be evenly applied and well raked in, bringing the soil to a final state that is relatively firm, yet with a good tilth on the surface.

PLANTING

Planting distances for outdoor tomatoes are in the region of 15–18in (38–45cm) apart in rows 30–50in (90–150cm) apart, running the rows north–south, if there are several, or east–west where only a few rows are planted, this being especially the case in south-facing borders backed by a south-facing wall.

Propagation and Time of Planting

Reference to the propagation programmes on pp75–7 will show that as the year progresses outdoor propagation takes less time, and this is due to the better light pattern. Planting of outdoor tomatoes is unlikely to be considered until around late May in the south (perhaps a little earlier in the Channel Islands) and early June in the north. Allowing the 4–6 weeks necessary for propagation, it can be seen that it is necessary to sow the seed around mid-April. Obviously if little heat is available, as is often the case where outdoor tomatoes are grown anyway, there will be a growth rate commensurate with prevailing temperatures.

Plants can be grown in $4^1/_4$in (11–12cm) pots or in large soil blocks and brought to first-truss-flowering stage in a cool greenhouse or raised in open cold frames before planting out firmly with the soil ball slightly below soil level, making sure the plants are fully acclimatised to outside conditions.

Establishment of Plants

Provided the plants are suitably hardened off and are not pot-bound (they may have been kept too long in their pots waiting for suitable planting weather), they should establish fairly rapidly, this being assisted by a light watering or spraying with clean water in hot weather. Stake immediately after planting (except for bush varieties – *see* p180) with canes. Some temporary shelter, especially from wind, can help establishment.

Plants inevitably assume a darker green colouration outdoors than plants growing in a greenhouse, and there can often be a tendency towards hardness of foliage, coupled with an upward curling of leaves, especially when cool nights follow warm days. This is because the carbohydrates manufactured during the day in the plants' leaves are not dissipated at night under cool conditions, as they would be in a warm greenhouse.

TRAINING AND GENERAL CULTURE

Plants are secured carefully to their canes, using soft twine or paper/wire clips, a practice which must be continued regularly throughout the development of the plant. Side shooting should be practised as for indoor tomatoes (except for bush varieties) and the plants pinched out above the third to fifth truss, according to the district and the exact situation involved. Obviously if growth is slow, as it can be in a cool summer, it may only be possible to ripen two or three trusses, remembering that once the fruit forms and increases in size, heat and warmth are still needed for ripening. Once a shine appears on the fruit, this is an indication that ripening is not far distant. On average in warm areas in a good season four trusses should be possible.

Plants must never be allowed to dry out and a mulch of straw or peat helps in this direction. Spraying overhead in very dry weather will help setting. Feeding should be carried out regularly every 10–14 days with a liquid feed (*see* p145). It is generally the case that medium-potash types are required for much of the season, rather than high-nitrogen feeds which tend to lower fruit quality – although the precise nature of feeding can be adjusted according to the stage of growth and date.

Bush or Dwarf Tomatoes

Cultural pattern is much the same, except that plants are not supported with canes or side shooted, merely being allowed to sprawl over the ground on a deep mulch of straw or low-set wire-netting. Modern breeding has produced bush tomatoes which are more productive at lower temperatures than 'standard' varieties. Some can be grown in pots and are ideal for a patio or balcony.

Cloche Culture

Several different techniques can be adopted using conventional cloches or polythene tunnels. Where cloches are to be used merely to start the crop off, planting out is usually carried out after the cloches have been in position for some 10–14 days to allow the soil to warm up. Planting can generally be carried out 2–3 weeks earlier than planting outdoors, and obviously there are greater benefits to be derived in exposed areas. Cloches can be removed when the plants have developed sufficiently, and the plants then staked and trained as for outdoor culture. In early September a mulch of straw can be laid down and the plants removed from their stakes and laid down under the cloches to allow green fruit to ripen, which it can do reasonably well in a good autumn. Polythene tunnels can be used in a similar manner.

Alternatively, if the cloches are large enough, and there are several elevated types of cloches available, the plants are grown under them throughout the full season. Humidity under the low polythene cover is a factor to be taken into account, and ventilation is important, as is regular watering despite any lateral movement of soil moisture. Training systems under cloches are varied, but generally involve running a wire horizontally on stakes 4in (10cm) or so below the top of the cloche, tying the plant to this. The number of trusses which can be grown under cloches varies enormously, and results are usually commensurate with the degree of care exercised. Some defoliation will definitely be required, as for greenhouse culture, but this should not be carried out to excess.

Bush varieties lend themselves admirably to full-season culture under cloches, the main point to watch being regular watering. It helps if trusses are supported on a low-set wire, or alternatively wire-netting kept a few inches above ground level.

Shading with a proprietary shading material, or lime and water may be necessary in extremely hot weather.

Pests and Diseases

These follow a similar pattern to greenhouse tomatoes – potato blight being the main outdoor plague.

Varieties

See general list of varieties (Chapter 13).

Appendices

1 The Economics of Tomato Production

It has been stated elsewhere in this book that few amateur gardeners are much concerned with the actual costs of producing their tomatoes. Their main objective is to grow worthwhile crops of good quality, fresh fruit of a variety they like. Things are very different with the commercial grower. With growers, it is vital that a good return on the investment required in production equipment is achieved, taking into account all the direct variable costs concerned with growing the crop, such as fuel and labour as well as all the general overheads of any business. It is true that the smaller general grower who has other strings to his bow, such as bedding plants, pot plants or flower crops in addition perhaps to outdoor-growing activities may well not look so critically at the economics of growing tomatoes which very often are treated as a 'catch' crop, but in my view it is pointless to grow anything commercially unless it yields a good return.

When presenting figures for a tomato costing on a commercial scale there are several key issues to take into account. Scale of production with the relationship this has to either wholesale marketing or direct retailing cannot be overlooked. Timing for the crop, along with regional variations in climate and the effect this has on fuel costs and yield is another vital issue. The figures produced by *The Grower* magazine are useful but are aimed at the specialist producer in the UK from the Midlands southwards, and across the water in Holland, and do not take into account the considerable areas of tomatoes grown in other regions, and often at a much less intensive level, and it is stressed that the following figures too must be taken only as a guide. The grower wishing an exact, detailed costing must look in detail at the particular site and scale of operation concerned.

Important Criteria with Regard to Tabular Information

The figures given in the table on p188 are per acre and per sq m. This would seem to be somewhat of a confusion of terms but the truth is that the acre is still considered as the large-scale unit of measurement, not only throughout the UK but farther afield. Reducing the scale to sq m one is able to have a ready comparison with producers in continental Europe. For those who wish to think in hectares, an acre is 0.4 of a hectare which means that it is fairly simple to convert acres to hectares (multiply by $2^1/_2$).

Plant Density

While it might be thought that this was a highly critical issue, it would not appear to be so – very close planting can tend to reduce yield and vice versa. The optimal $2-2^1/_2$ plants per sq yd (2.62 plants/m^2) is taken as the norm.

Yields

These will be graded 'basic', 'moderate' and 'optimum' at 50, 100 and 150 tons per acre and the actual figures per m^2 are given in the table.

Gross Income

This is obviously the most important issue of all and the problem is that prices vary seasonally and from region to region. Tomatoes in the UK at any rate are still largely sold per pound which tends to be a complication when thinking in terms of kg/sq m. This can be overcome by referring to the gross yields/acre in tons and the weight in lb/sq m. A wholesale price of 30p/lb is taken as an average figure but it is felt that, for Scotland especially, the figure could be 36p/lb which means adding 20 per cent to the gross income. In recent years this 'premium' has tended to be less predictable, although prices are generally higher in the north.

Marketing

The figures given in the table have been calculated on a percentage basis related to gross income and the figure of 19 per cent is considered realistic. Note, however, that in Scotland when higher prices could prevail, a lower-percentage marketing figure could be acceptable. On direct selling in its many varieties it is often felt that marketing costs may well be lower, particularly if direct retailing in any quantity is involved. Nevertheless, marketing in any form does take time and effort and it would be unrealistic not to allow a reasonable percentage.

Variable Costs

These include all the costs concerned with production, including fuel usage, plants, growing modules, carbon dioxide, fertilisers, sprays, water, electricity, biological control, polythene (for laying on floor), twine and other sundry items. These have been calculated on the percentage basis of 32 per cent of gross income. It is the only practical way of treating things on a generalised basis. A point of some importance here is that fuel costs will obviously vary regionally but it may well be that higher fuel usage in Scotland, for example, would be compensated for by the higher market prices.

Gross Margins

This is the gross income figure from which marketing and variable costs have been deducted.

Labour Costs (1988)

Charges for labour vary from around £3/hr (casual) to £3.80/hr and have been calculated at 15 per cent of gross income. A note of warning here is the situation where yields are not commensurate with the input of labour due to the reducing factors occasioned by weather patterns, disease or other issues. The actual hours of labour as recorded by *The Grower* vary from just over 8,500 hours/ha to just short of 13,000 hours/ha which reduced to acreage terms is just under 3,500 hours to 5,200 hours. The cost of labour is given in the summary but note the proviso that labour costs may well be higher than this for the 100 ton/acre crop.

Net Returns

In the table these are given per acre and per sq m. The net return is not truly profit as it does not take into account the overheads in running the business, nor indeed the servicing of capital which is generally taken at around the 15 per cent level, although this obviously varies. It can be seen, therefore, that taking into account a capital investment in excess of £100,000/acre and a servicing charge of 15 per cent (£15,000), the profit margin is very quickly whittled down to an uneconomic level, whereas at high cropping levels the net return is acceptable. Many growers are trying to set up or take over existing glass for a much lower figure, or are considering plastic structures, especially when a new project is planned. By the same token, if it were possible to reduce fuel costs dramatically because of the availability of waste heat, the burning of straw or wood or other methods of low-cost fuelling, an entirely different complexion can be thrown on things, especially when one studies the cost/therm of various fuels (*see* p189). In broad terms, if one were considering the utilisation of waste energy from a factory, power station or other source, it would be necessary to negotiate an attractive tariff rate. The problem with many waste-energy projects lies in the necessity to provide standby plant to take over should the factory cease functioning for any reason.

It has been estimated that fuel costs for conventional fuel would be in the region of £14,000–16,000 per annum (per acre) or 20–30 per cent less with double-skinned plastics or thermal screens.

It cannot be stressed too strongly that these are guide figures only. As yields drop and, taking into account fixed costs and capital for servicing and depreciation, it can be seen that break-even can be arrived at. Very often in a family, labour is not charged out against a crop, which makes a profound difference to the general economic picture.

Tomato Costings at Different Cropping Levels (under glass)
(Rounded-off figures in £s per acre)

Yields		Gross income*		Marketing costs		Variable costs**		Gross margin		Labour costs		Net return	
tons/ acre	kg/ m² (lb)	acre	m²	acre	m²	acre	m²	acre	m²	acre	m²	acre	m²
50	13 (6)	36,700	9.10	7,000	1.75	11,800	2.9	18,000	4.50	5,700	1.41	12,000	3
100	26 (12)	73,000	18.25	14,000	3.50	23,600	5.90	35,400	8.85	12,000	2.83	24,000	6
150	38 (18)	111,000	27.50	21,000	5.25	35,500	8.87	53,000	13.75	17,000	4.25	36,000	9

* See note above on regional price variations
** Calculated, as stated, on a 32 per cent norm, but a variable figure according to timing etc: could be 15–25 per cent higher for fuel.

Comparative Fuel Prices (February 1988) (Bulk purchase)
Prices of fuel vary from time to time and regionally

Fuel	Cost per litre delivered	Base Cost/therm (100,000Btu)	Actual cost allowing for efficiency losses/therm (100,000Btu)
Oil			
HFO	7p/litre	17–18p	19–20p
MFO 950 sec	8p/litre	20–21p	25–26p
LFO 200 sec	9p/litre	21–22p	26–28p
Gas oil 35 sec	10.25p/litre	27–28p	33–34p
Natural gas			
Net cost 34–36p/ therm*			42–43p
Coal** based on current prices of between £50 and £75/ton		16–24p	20–30p
Straw, wood etc			
Based on straw (at £10/ton)		7–8p	12–13p
Electricity (100 per cent efficient) Cost at various unit prices (unit = 3,412Btu)	Cost/unit 2p 3p 4p 5p 6p		Cost/therm (100,000Btu) 58p 87p 116p 145p 174p

* Note Cheaper tariff available on 'interrupted supplies'. Liquid gas prices approximately plus 25 per cent.
** Note Coal has a varying calorific value.
*** Note Figures are rounded off for convenience. With the exception of straw, actual cost figures are based on modern boilers of between 75 and 80 per cent efficiency.

Explanation of terms and metric conversion

HFO Heavy FVUEL Oil
MFO Medium Fuel Oil
LFO Light Fuel Oil

1Btu = 1.055 kJ
1 therm = 100,000Btu = 105.5mJ
1Btu/lb = 2326 J/kg therefore mJ/kg × 430 = Btu/lb
1kg = 2.20462lb

= 29.3 kWh

2 Tomato Grading

Important legislation was introduced in Britain during 1964 – the Agriculture and Horticulture Act – which provides for 'extending the provision for assisting by way of the paying of grant the production and marketing of horticultural produce, and the imposing of requirements as to the grading of horticultural produce'. Commercial growers are now eligible for grants for the building of new and the replacement of old glasshouses, packing houses, grading machinery, modernisation of heating systems and many other specialised appliances and buildings. Statutory grading of specific horticultural crops followed this legislation and tomatoes, the subject of this book, were no exception. Statutory grading for this crop began on 13 May 1968, and supersedes the voluntary grading of the now defunct Tomato and Cucumber Marketing Board. It applies to tomatoes sold only through wholesale channels, which may be defined as wholesale markets, individual wholesalers' premises, grower/wholesalers, packing stations and depots for chain stores and supermarkets.

Grading-scheme inspections are undertaken by horticultural marketing inspectors (marketing officers in Scotland), who inspect consignments selected at random. The grades comprise requirements as to development, ripeness, colour, shape, cleanliness, progressive and non-progressive defects, blemish and sizing, and fall into four distinct classes: Extra Class and Classes I, II and III, in that order of merit.

3 Nutrient Film Technique (NFT), Mineral Rockwool Culture and Perlite Culture

NFT

The layout and design of NFT systems can follow many varied patterns. For tomatoes, cucumbers and other 'tall' crops, plastic sloping gullies are laid on either sloping ground, sloping boards, elevated sloping metal stands, polystyrene slabs or flat surfaces generally, and carry a film of constantly re-circling nutrient solution.

Recent years have seen much change in physical design, from rigid pre-formed plastic gullies, to cheaper thin-film plastic gullies using thin-gauge black/white polythene with or without a base layer of capillary matting. It is usual to design these gullies with a slope of not less than 1–100 and more recently with a 'platform' in the middle so that plants can stay proud of the nutrient. The basic object is to have an even film of nutrient not greater than $1/4$in (6–7mm). The gulley width lies between 9 and 12in (22.5–30cm). Adjustable stands may be used to create a suitable slope to keep the nutrient moving quickly. The basic layout and design of a nutrient system is shown in Fig 52. Systems can be any size but obviously must be tailored to the size of

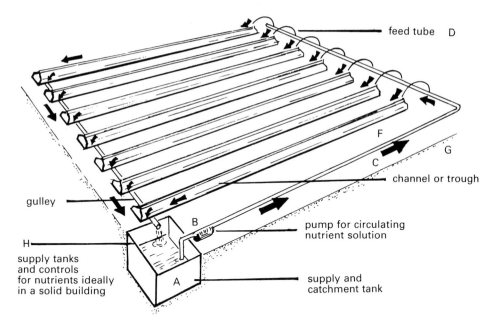

feed tube D

F

G

C

channel or trough

gulley

pump for circulating
nutrient solution

H

supply tanks
and controls
for nutrients ideally
in a solid building

B

A

supply and
catchment tank

Fig 52 Layout for nutrient film growing

unit available. The UK chemical company ICI states that the nutrient sump
should be of a capacity of 500gal per acre (5,550 litres/ha) for a protected
crop in temperate zones. Due to transpiration and evaporation losses probably
greater reserve is needed in tropical climates.

Firms providing NFT equipment will quote pump sizes necessary for
different scales of units and also supply all the fitments although it is feasible
to install systems on a 'do-it-yourself' basis and probably cheaper too.

Referring to Fig 52 the main elements are lettered as follows:

A Supply tank on the basis of 500gal per acre (5,500 litres/ha).
B Pump of adequate size for size of unit, submersible or an outside type.
C Supply pipe or pipes to troughs, usually $1/_2$in–2in (1.25–5cm), made of
polythene or alkathene.
D Feed tubes invariably of $1/_4$in (6mm) diameter.
E Troughs rigid or made up with polystyrene centre platform or made up
with black/white polythene (white outside) 12–14in wide (30–35cm).
F Metal tray on stands or soil, adjusted to give sufficient slope, which should
not be less than 1–100.
G Gulley flowing back to supply tank – note that filters will be required,
size of fittings related to number of outlets.
H According to levels of sophistication, nutrient-supply concentrate-tank
along with nutrient-monitoring control-gear as specified by design. Facilities for heating nutrient solution – a submersible electric heater or other
method – are invariably necessary in temperate zones, to maintain it at
around 77°F (25°C).

Nutrient Control

Obviously the most critical aspect of NFT is nutrient control: supplying the plants with the correct balance of nutrients relative to the water supply of the area and maintaining this according to crop uptake of nutrients, evaporation loss and so on.

On a very small scale, nutrient replacement every few weeks can be effective and avoids complications. In other cases first and foremost an analysis of water supply is necessary, not only for pH but for the presence or absence of various elements. These include magnesium, calcium, iron, manganese, molybdenum, copper, chlorine and zinc. Where this analysis shows large quantities of trace elements to be present in the water supply, a 'starter' solution and self-formulated or specially prescribed feeds may be necessary if these trace elements are not quickly to build up to toxic levels. Having analysed the water supply, several different courses of action can be taken. You can:

1 Decide to control manually the monitoring of nutrients on the basis of pH (by liquid indicator or pH meter) and conductivity levels in microsiemens (mho) per 2,500–3,000 tomatoes using a conductivity meter.
2 Install 'automatic' controllers which monitor and adjust pH and nutrient levels.
3 Purchase proprietary feeds and follow the full directions given with these.

Mineral Rockwool Culture

A feature of rockwool culture, in common with 'hydro-cultural' systems for potplants (perlite etc), is the need to grow plants from the outset in the chosen medium. This is not only to avoid fungal infection but also because of the nature of the roots which form, as these react unfavourably to changes in substratum. It is therefore essential to use rockwool propagating blocks. Seed can be sown directly into a slit in small cubes. It is also suitable to raise seedlings in some inert medium such as perlite and prick out into rockwool blocks. The blocks must be wet with the warmed nutrient solution before sowing or pricking out and are placed on polythene, being fed with the nutrient solution at each watering, and spaced out as described under traditional plant raising with a watering system. The small cubes are fitted into larger ones. The layout of plants has been broadly described in Chapter 8 but details specific to rockwool culture are given below. Vertical mineral rockwool has recently become available.

Slabs of expanded polystyrene are ideally placed beneath the rockwool to prevent downward movement of heat. These slabs should be 2in (5cm) thick at least and grooved out to accommodate 1in (20mm) alkathene pipes above the slabs (*see* Fig 53). These pipes are run at a temperature of around 103°F (40°C) to keep the rockwool mat at about 74–77°F

(23–25°C). It may be necessary to have a separate take-off from the boiler for this purpose.

Rockwool slabs are 3ft x 6in x 3in (90 x 15 x 7.5cm) for tomatoes and are placed end to end and wrapped in black/white polythene in threes to prevent movement of water and nutrients due to any slope. Nails are used to hold the polythene in place – these must not be galvanised. Failing this, use adhesive tape.

To set out the plants, merely stand them on the growing slabs – previously wetted with nutrients – at the outset using one drip nozzle in each plant, letting the nozzles drip on to the rockwool slabs

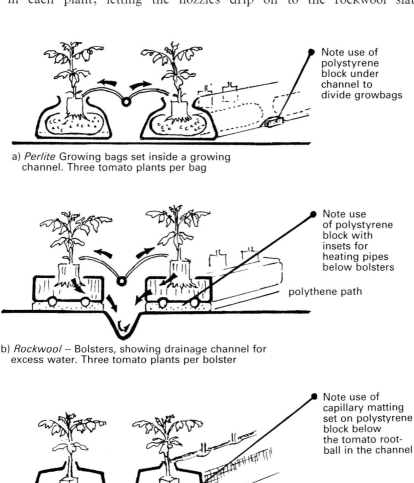

Note use of polystyrene block under channel to divide growbags

a) *Perlite* Growing bags set inside a growing channel. Three tomato plants per bag

Note use of polystyrene block with insets for heating pipes below bolsters

polythene path

b) *Rockwool* – Bolsters, showing drainage channel for excess water. Three tomato plants per bolster

Note use of capillary matting set on polystyrene block below the tomato root-ball in the channel

c) *Nutrient Film Growing*, showing polythene channel containing a 1/12–1/10in (2-3mm) film of circulating nutrient solution

Fig 53 Systems of growing in inert media or solution

when the plants have been established. It may also be necessary to make slits in the side of the polythene to allow excess nutrients to drain off.

Nutrient Solutions

At the propagation stage a proprietary feed such as Nutriflora T is satisfactory, and after planting, two stock solutions are made up based on the analyses of the water supply, as with NFT. Stockbridge House recommends two nutrient solutions be given alternately at each watering, preferably through the conductivity meter. Further emphasis is made of the need to check the pH and conductivity of the solution in the growing slabs and the recommendation is that the pH should be between 6 and 6.5 and the conductivity 2,500 to 3,000 microsiemens.

PERLITE CULTURE

The general layout of perlite culture is shown in Fig 53 and details of the method are best obtained from the West of Scotland Agricultural College (*see* Appendix 4) or suppliers of perlite.

4 USEFUL ADDRESSES

Biological Control:
Bunting and Sons
The Nurseries
Great Horkesley
Colchester CO6 4AJ
Tel: (0206) 271300

The Grower Magazine
50 Doughty Street
London WC1N 2CS
Tel: 01 405 03364
(They publish a Reference Special giving a full list of up-to-date addresses).

Perlite Culture:
West of Scotland Agricultural College
Auchincruive
By Ayr KY6 5AW
Tel: 0292 520331

D T Brown & Co Ltd
Station Road
Poulton-Le-Fylde
Blackpool FY6 7HX
Tel: Poulton-Le-Fylde 882371

Sutton Seeds Ltd
Hele Road
Torquay TQ2 7QT
Tel: Torquay 62011

British Agrochemicals Association
4 Lincoln Court
Lincoln Road
Peterborough PR1 2RP
Tel: 0733 49225

British Commercial Glasshouse
   Manufacturers' Association
c/o Cambridge Glasshouse Co Ltd
Comberton
Cambridge CB3 7BY
Tel: 0223 262395

British Institute of Agricultural
   Consultants
c/o Durleigh House
3 Elm Close
Campton, Shefford,
Beds SG17 5PE
Tel: 0462 813380

British Organic Farmers
86/88 Colston Street
Bristol BS1 5BB
Tel: 0272 299666

Farm Shop & Pick Your Own
  Association
NFU, Agriculture House
Knightsbridge
London SW1X 7NJ
Tel: 01 235 5077

Highlands and Islands Development
  Board
Bridge House
27 Bank Street
Inverness IV1 1QR
Tel: 0463 234171 ext 246/482

Horticultural Trades Association
19 High Street
Theale
Reading, Berks RG7 5AH
Tel: 0734 303132

Institute of Horticulture
PO Box 313
80 Vincent Square
Westminster
London SW1P 2PE
Tel: 01 834 4333

MAFF Publications
Lion House
Willowburn Trading Estate
Alnwick, Northumberland NE66 2PF
Tel: 0665 602881

Pesticides Registration and
  Surveillance Department
Ministry of Agriculture, Fisheries and
  Food
Harpenden Laboratory
Hatching Green
Harpenden, Herts AL5 2BD
Tel: 05827 5241

Royal Horticultural Society
80 Vincent Square
Westminster
London SW1P 2PE
Tel: 01 834 4333

Royal Horticultural Society's Garden
Wisley
Woking
Surrey GU23 6QB
Tel: 0483 224234

Scottish Agricultural Organisation
  Society Ltd
19 Claremont Crescent
Edinburgh EH7 4JW
Tel: 031 556 6574

Soil Association Ltd (Organic
  Growing)
86/88 Colston Street
Bristol, Avon BS1 5BB
Tel: 0272 290661

Rockwool Culture:
Pilkington Insulation Ltd
PO Box 10
St Helens
Merseyside WA10 3MS
Tel: 0744 693220

Brinkman (Horticultural Services)
  UK Ltd
Stur Road
Quarry Lane
Chichester
West Sussex PO19 2RP
Tel: 0243 531666

NFT Culture:
Duntech Irrigation Services Ltd
Lashlake Nurseries
Chinnor Road
Towersey
Thame
Oxon OX9 3QZ
Tel: 084 4215411

Stapley Contracts Ltd
High House Farm
Kenordington
Ashford
Kent TM26 2LZ
Tel: 023 373 2006

Horticultrual Product News
201/205 Kingston Road
Leatherhead
Surrey KT22 7PB
Tel: 0372 370177

5 GETTING ADVICE

Charges are now made for most aspects of advisory work through Government financed services (ADAS in England and Wales, the Agricultural Colleges in Scotland and the Department of Agriculture in Ireland). Their HQ addresses and telephone numbers are listed.

Advice is also available from a wide variety of private consultants – many of whom were formerly with official services – or in commerce. These will also have to be paid for. They are generally known by repute.

Advisers employed by various supply firms or institutions such as banks or financial bodies vary in their role in many have direct sales responsibilities while others have not. They can be contacted through their respective firms or bodies and their services are generally free, although this should be established before becoming committed. Help, advice and training are available at many colleges.

Agricultural Development Advisory Services (ADAS)

For details of all Advisory Services in England and Wales

Headquarters:
Great Westminster House
Horseferry Road,
London SW1P 2AE
Tel: 01 216 6311

National Advisory Services

For details of all Advisory
Services in Northern Ireland

Headquarters:
Department of Agriculture
Horticulture Division
Greenmount College of Agriculture
and Horticulture
Antrim BT41 4PU
Tel: 08494 62114

For details of all Advisory Services
in Scotland

East:
Edinburgh and East of Scotland
College
West Mains Road
Kings Buildings
Edinburgh
Tel: 031 667 1041

North:
North of Scotland College of
    Agriculture
Horticulture Division
School of Agriculture
581 King Street
Aberdeen
Tel: 0224 40291

West and Central:
West of Scotland Agricultural College
Horticulture Department
57 High Street
Lanark ML11 7LF
Tel: 0555 2562

For details of all Advisory Services
    in Eire

Headquarters:
Agriculture House
Kildare Street
Dublin 2
Tel: 0001 789011

Main Research Centres in Britain having Interests in Tomatoes

Glasshouse Investigational Unit for
    Scotland
Coylton Road
Auchincruive
By Ayr KA6 5HN
Tel: 0292 520331/520419

Efford EHS
Lymington
Hampshire S04 0LZ
Tel: 0590 73341

Stockbridge House EHS
Cawood
Selby
N Yorks YO8 0TZ
Tel: 0757 86 275/276

Guernsey Horticultural Experimental
    Station
St Martin's
Guernsey
Tel: 0481 35741

Index

Abortion, flower, 169
Advisory services, 197–8
AFRC Institute, Silsoe, 21
Aggregate, 93, 94, 106, 117, 118, 148–9
Agriculture and Horticulture Act (1964), 190
'Ailsa Craig', 6, 160, 179
'Alicante', 179
America, 69
Ammonia, 49, 50, 96, 111–13 passim, 148, 154, 174
Aphids, 165, 172, 173

Bag culture, 4, 55, 64, 73, 93–4, 94, 106–8, 118–19, 122, 129, 150, 157, 183

Balch, Alan, 6
Bark, wood, 69
Basamid, 177, 178
Benches, 36–7, 36
Benlate, 171
Benomyl, 157, 158
'Black bottoms' (blossom end rot), 45, 50, 94, 146, 147, 168, 173
'Blue Book', 154
Border culture, 4, 73, 92, 94, 96, 105, 107–15, 127–9, 145–8
Boron, 48, 54, 167
Botrytis, 9, 139, 151, 153, 159, 171, 173
British Agrochemicals Association, 153
'Bronzing', 161, 168, 171
Bush/dwarf varieties, 132, 180–1, 184, 185

Calcium, 48, 51, 52, 59, 63, 147, 167, 192
Carbon bisulphide, 177
Channel Islands, 182, 183
Chemicals, 48, 153–4, 160, 165, 170, 176–8 see also individual headings
Chempak, 72, 122, 144
Cheshunt Research Station, 175; Compound, 155
Chlorine, 48, 192
Chlorosis, 53, 54
Chloropicrin, 177
Climate, 7-9 passim, 91, 186
Cloche culture, 185

CO_2, 35, 42–3, 50, 93, 120, 141
Colouration, 49, 52–4 passim, 142, 143, 162, 184
Composts, 64–73, 77, 79, 81, 83, 112, 117–18, 182
Copper, 48, 54, 60, 155, 159, 168, 192
Costs, 11, 22, 30, 108, 186–90 passim; fuel, 11, 22, 186, 188; labour, 188
Cresylic acid, 151, 164
Cropping double, 122
Cuttings, 74

D-D, 164, 177
Damping-down, 33, 34, 45, 105, 173
Damping off, 154–5, 173
Dazomet, 177
Didymella, 155, 158–9
Digging, 109, 111, 182
Disease, 49, 61, 91–3 passim, 96, 107, 120, 132, 139, 153–63, 171, 173, 174, 177, 179 see also individual headings
Disinfectants, 75, 90 see also individual headings
Dithane, 156, 161, 177
Drainage, 10, 17, 108, 109, 117, 119, 182
Dry set, 105, 169

Eelworm, 61, 92, 108, 109, 117, 120, 148, 151, 155, 163–4, 171, 175, 176, 183; root knot, 164, 171
Efford EHS, 22

Fairfield Experimental Station, 106
Farmyard manure, 111-13, 147, 148, 182, 183
Feeding, 35–6, 61–5, 62, 79, 87, 93, 94, 119, 131, 143–50, 168, 184 see also Nutrients; foliar, 147, 162, 164, 168; osmotic, 131, 144
Fertilisation, 9, 45, 140, 143, 149, 161, 169
Fertilisers, 35–6, 44, 54–5, 61, 63–5, 72–3, 83, 96, 113–15, 121–2, 131, 145–50, 174, 183; dilution, 35, 65, 131, 146
Flooding, 96, 105, 112–13, 115

Flowers, 10, 45, 50, 52, 75, 86, 126–7, 140, 141, 143, 159, 169–70
Formaldehyde, 151, 177; urea, 69
Frost protection, 11, 26
Fruit, 5, 10, 42, 45, 50, 52, 54, 126, 139, 140, 146, 147, 149–52, 159–62, 165–9 passim, 171, 173, 184, 185; splitting, 169, 173
Fungi, parasitic, 117, 130, 153–5
Fungicides, 155–7, 159–61, 171, 177 see also individual headings
Fusarium, 89, 155, 157–8

Germany, 69
Germination, 74–5, 79–80, 162
Grading, 150, 190
Grafting, 4, 83, 87–90, 92, 116, 149, 158, 163
Grants, 190
Greece, 6
Greenback, 168, 173
Greenhouses, 4, 6, 7, 10–40, 14, 16, 18, 19, 28, 29, 74, 91, 105, 108–9, 123, 151–3; equipment, 25–40; lining, 39–40, 39, 155; mobile, 17–19; plastic, 19–22, 24
Growbags see Bag culture
Growing rooms, 37–8, 37

Heat/heating, 9, 11, 23, 25–30, 32–3, 91, 124, 126, 151; conservation, 21–3; loss, 25, 39–40; sterilisation, 162, 163, 175–6
Hoddesdon method, 175
Holland, 6, 109, 140, 175, 186
Hormones, 143, 167
Humidity, 8–9, 22, 44, 80, 94, 105, 126, 130, 149, 151, 153, 155, 159, 169, 171, 185
Hydroponics, 70, 94, 96, 120, 129, 131
Hygiene, 35, 74, 75, 90, 105, 116, 151–2, 154–5, 158, 159, 162, 165, 166

ICI, 144, 191
Income, 187
Insecticides, 164–6 passim, 172
Investment, 186, 188
Iron, 48, 53–4, 60, 168, 192

Isle of Wight, 162
Italy, 6

Jeyes Fluid, 152, 156, 164

Lea Valley Station, 21
Leaves, 43, 139–40, 142, 161,
  164–8 passim, 170, 171, 173;
  curl, 41, 45, 49, 162, 167, 169,
  184; discolouration, 52–4
  passim, 142, 157, 161–3 passim,
  167, 169, 171; mould disease,
  153, 157, 160, 171, 173;
  removal, 139–40, 140, 168
Leafminer, 165–6, 172, 173
Light/lighting, 8–13 passim, 20,
  23, 38–9, 45, 49, 74, 75, 80, 84,
  85, 91, 108, 123, 125, 126, 141,
  143, 169
Lime, 59, 71, 113, 148, 157, 167,
  183; hydrated, 59, 113
Loam, 65–6, 70, 71

Magnesium, 48, 52–3, 60, 64,
  113–15 passim, 147, 168, 192
Manganese, 48, 54, 60, 168, 192
Marketing, 187; inspectors, 190
Maxicrop, 93
Metham-sodium, 167, 177
Methyl bromide, 177, 178
Mice, 166, 172
Millipedes, 166, 172
Mineral disorders, 166–7
Molybdenum, 48, 192
'Moneymaker', 159, 160, 164,
  179
Moth, tomato, 166, 172
Mulching, 147–8, 148, 157, 158,
  164, 171, 184, 185

Nematodes, 89 see also PCN
Nitram, 163
Nitro-chalk, 121, 163, 171
Nitrogen, 49–50, 55, 59, 63, 69,
  93, 111, 114, 121, 127, 131,
  144, 146, 147, 149, 150, 163,
  168, 170
Nutrients/Nutrition, 10, 44–55,
  61–5, 62, 70, 71, 91, 96, 109,
  111, 113–15, 119, 141–50, 159,
  166, 182, 192, 194 see also
  Feeding; Fertilisers
Nutrient film technique (NFT),
  4, 35, 64, 73, 94, 95, 96, 106,
  120, 129–31, 143, 145, 190–2,
  191
Nutriflora T, 194

Oedema, 169
Organic growing, 47, 48, 53, 70,
  92, 93, 109, 112, 122, 154, 183
Osmosis, 44–5, 131, 144, 146
Outdoor culture, 13, 161, 182–5

Paper, waste, 69
Peat, 4, 45, 67, 70–2 passim, 111,
  112, 119, 129, 131, 146–8

passim, 157, 182, mattress
  system, 93, 120
Perlite, 4, 45, 64, 68, 70, 73, 81,
  94, 119, 124, 129, 143, 145,
  149, 176, 194
Pests, 92, 93, 107, 120, 155, 163–
  7, 171–2, 173, 174, 177 see also
  individual headings
Phenol, 177
Phosphorus, 48, 50–2, 59, 63–5
  passim, 114, 167
Photosynthesis, 42–3, 49, 52–4
  passim, 75, 126, 132, 141, 161
Physiology, 41–55, 91, 167–70
Phytophthora, 89, 154, 161, 185
Picking, 75–7, 150–2, 150
Planting, 12, 75–7, 123–9, 127,
  183, 185, 194; density, 123–4,
  183, 187
Pollination, 33, 45, 46, 105
Polystyrene, 68–9
Polyurethane, 68–9
Portugal, 6
Potassium, 48, 52, 59, 63–5
  passim, 114, 115, 131, 144,
  146, 147, 150, 167, 170
Potato cyst nematode (PCN), 61,
  108, 109, 117, 148, 151, 163–4,
  171, 173, 174, 183
Pots/potting, 75–7, 80–4, 81,
  93–4, 120
Prices, 187
Pricking off, 37, 80, 83, 162
Programming, crop, 75–7, 183,
  186
Propagation, 9, 36–7, 37, 74–90,
  169, 183
Pruning, 139–40, 139, 184

Radiation, 9–11 passim, 20, 23,
  28, 30, 123, 126
Red spider mite, 164–5, 172, 173
Resistance, disease, 6, 52, 89, 90,
  92, 153, 155, 158, 160, 162–5,
  179
Respiration, 41, 74, 132
Returns, net, 188
Ring culture, 64, 73, 92–3 94,
  106, 116–18, 129, 148–50
Rockwool, 4, 35, 45, 64, 69, 70,
  73, 79, 81–3, 82, 94, 119, 120,
  124, 129, 143, 145, 149, 176,
  192–4, 193
Roots, 10, 43, 60, 92–4 passim,
  107, 111, 116, 118, 130–2, 148,
  149, 151, 155–7, 163–4, 170;
  brown/corky, 89, 156
Rootstock, 4, 89, 92, 158, 164,
  171, 180
Rot, blossom end see Black
  Bottoms; buck eye, 160–1, 171;
  root, 109, 151, 153, 155–8
  passim, stem 160, 171

Salt, 44, 45, 60, 64, 65, 83, 92–
  4 passim, 96, 105, 112–15
  passim, 117, 129–31, passim,

142, 144, 145, 147, 150, 170
Sand, 68, 70, 71, 94, 109, 119
Scorching, 146, 156, 162
Scotland, 6, 85, 187; West of –
  Agricultural College, 194
Seed, 74–5, 89, 162
Selling, direct, 187
Setting, 127, 143, 161, 184
Shading, 12, 123, 157, 184
Shelter, 13–15 passim, 23, 24,
  182, 184
Side-shoots, 54, 139, 167, 184
Silvering, 172
Smokes, 159, 165
Soil, 47–8, 55–61, 71, 92, 96,
  105–9, 111–14 passim, 124,
  126, 128, 130, 156, 157, 174–8,
  182; analysis, 55–61, 108, 113
Soil Association, 112, 154
Soil-less culture, 4, 69–73, 81,
  93–4, 116–20 passim, 143, 183
  see also individual headings
Sowing, 75–9, 78, 183
Spacing, 75–7, 86, 121, 122, 124,
  125, 128, 129, 183
Spain, 6, 109
Spraying, 33, 105, 147, 161, 162,
  165, 172, 184
Springtails, 164, 172
Stems, 158–9, 160, 162, 166,
  168–71 passim; rot, 160, 171
Sterilisation, 4, 50, 66, 107, 108,
  111, 112, 114, 116, 117, 153,
  154, 156, 158, 160, 162–4,
  passim, 171, 172, 174–8;
  chemical 4, 162, 163, 176–8,
  183; heat, 55, 96, 162, 163,
  175–6
Stockbridge House, 194
Stopping, 140, 140
Straw-bale culture, 4, 9, 43, 64,
  93, 94, 95, 105, 106, 112, 120–
  2, 129, 136, 145, 149, 150
Suckers, 90, 139
Sulphur, 48, 54, 165, 168
Support, 87, 133–4, 133, 184, 185
Symphylids, 164, 172

Temperature, 9, 23, 25–9, 38, 44,
  45, 74, 80, 84–6, 121, 126, 128,
  132, 141, 143, 158, 162, 167–
  70 passim; soil/compost, 92, 93,
  118, 122, 124, 128, 129, 143,
  175–7
Tensiometers, 105–6
Thrips, 165, 172
Tissue, analysis, 60; culture, 74
'Totem', 132
Training, 124, 134–8, 135, 137,
  138, 184, 185
Translocation, 45
Transpiration, 43–4, 130, 132,
  157
Tri-sodium ortho-phosphate, 75,
  90, 162
Trough culture, 94, 119–20, 129,
  145

U-value, 25–7

Van Post scale, 67
Varieties, 179–81
Vascular disease, 151, 153
Ventilation, 15, 21, 24, 31–2, 45, 91, 130, 138, 155, 157, 159, 160, 169, 171
Vermiculite, 68, 119, 176
Verticillium, 89, 157–8
Virus disease, 74, 75, 109, 111, 117, 120, 151, 153, 161–3, 171, *173*, 174, 176

Vitax, 72, 122, 144

Water, 33, 43–5, 48, 52, 91, 96, 105–6, 141–2, 167, 169, 170, 192
Watering, 33–5, *34*, 45, 50, 79, 80, 86–7, 93, 94, 96, 105–6, 112, 119, 128–32, 146–9 *passim*, 151, 168, 171, 184, 185
Waterlogging, 50, 92, 94
Way, W. D. 20
Weedkiller, 17, 93, 111, 117, 167
Weeds, 17, 92, 109, 111, 148, 169, 174, 177
White fly, 165, 172, *173*
Wilt/Wilting, 131, 149, 157–8, 163, 164, 169, 171; spotted, 162; *see also* Fusarium; Vascular disease
Wireworms, 155, 166, 172, 183
Woodlice (slaters), 155, 166, 172
Wright, H. B., 175

Yields, 4, 119, 123, 152, 186, 187, 190

Zinc, 48, 60, 192